**'I have no intenti...
position you find...**

But all Charlie could ...
caressed her, how he had kissed ...
wanted was to feel his arms around her again.
'But you *do* want me,' she pleaded, her eyes
misty as they gazed up into his. 'I know you
do.'

Dear Reader

Welkom! This month we welcome you to the beautiful city of Amsterdam, in the Netherlands, famous for its canals, its intriguing history, its art and culture—and, of course, its lively and exciting nightlife! It's a city with many faces—and we're sure you'll agree that Susanne McCarthy makes you feel you're there. All this and romance too!

The Editor

The author says:

'I love to travel, but I'm not the beach or the museum type. I love to wander around city streets, finding my own way, maybe stopping to ask directions as an excuse to strike up a conversation; I love to sit in a café, and soak up the atmosphere.

'Amsterdam is one of my favourite cities. It's beautifully preserved but it's no museum. It's young, lively and liberal—and so friendly that you feel at home on your first day there.'

Susanne McCarthy

*TURN TO THE BACK PAGES OF THIS BOOK FOR *WELCOME TO EUROPE*...OUR FASCINATING FACT-FILE*

DIAMOND HEART

BY
SUSANNE McCARTHY

MILLS & BOON LIMITED
ETON HOUSE   18-24 PARADISE ROAD
RICHMOND   SURREY   TW9 1SR

First published in Great Britain 1992
by Mills & Boon Limited

© Susanne McCarthy 1992

Australian copyright 1992
Philippine copyright 1993
This edition 1993

ISBN 0 263 77898 3

Set in Times Roman 10½ on 12 pt.
01-9302-51269 C

Made and printed in Great Britain

European Community

1	EIRE	4	NETHERLANDS	7	GERMANY	10	FRANCE
2	U.K.	5	BELGIUM	8	PORTUGAL	11	ITALY
3	DENMARK	6	LUXEMBOURG	9	SPAIN	12	GREECE

CHAPTER ONE

'OH, NO—this really is too much!'

Pieter den Ouden threw down his pen with an impatient sigh and rose from his desk, where he had been working on the specifications for a very large order of precision-tooled helical gears for a French aerospace company. Even the efficient double-glazing at the window couldn't dampen the blast of sound coming up from the houseboat moored below.

They probably didn't even have a licence to moor there, he reflected irritably, resting his hands high against the window-frame to look down at the dilapidated vessel. No new boats were supposed to moor here on the Herengracht, unless they were replacing old ones. This one had just suddenly arrived a few days ago, and the horde of young people who lived on it seemed to have held a noisy party every night since then.

He twisted his wrist to glance at his watch. Almost midnight—he was surprised no one had rung the police to complain. But then, this part of the Herengracht was mostly occupied by banks and businesses—he had few neighbours, except those who, like himself, had chosen to maintain the convenience of an apartment above their offices.

Almost midnight—and he was still working. With a wry smile he ran his hand back through his thick blond hair. Was he becoming a workaholic? Janine had accused him of that only the other day, com-

7

plaining that she spoke to his secretary more often than she spoke to him.

And maybe she had a point, he conceded fairly. He *was* a little inclined to run his private life with the same clockwork precision with which he ran his business, fitting it into his busy schedule—Janine on Mondays and Saturdays, Ingrid on Wednesdays and every other Friday.

But he liked to work hard. In the ten years since he had inherited the small family engineering firm of Den Ouden's he had transformed it from a moderately successful domestic concern into a powerful international company. He had found, rather to his surprise, that he had a flair for business, and what had started out as a cold duty he would have given anything to avoid had become almost a pleasure. Almost . . .

The sounds of music and laughter drifted up to him from the canal below. The kids had painted the boat in bright swirls of psychedelic colour that brought back to him a tugging reminder of his own youth. And someone clearly had the desire to be a gardener—there were colourful pots of geraniums and begonias crammed into every available nook and cranny, and balanced along the gunwale, inches above the murky waters of the canal.

He was about to turn away when he saw the girl again. She had been there since the boat had first arrived—she must be one of the ones who actually lived on it. He found himself watching her with a kind of strange fascination. She was dancing on the roof of the boat, barefoot. Her hair was a wild tumble of blonde curls, laced with bits of coloured ribbon, that tossed around her shoulders as she danced, and her clothes were an eclectic collection of jumble from the flea-market on Waterlooplein. The sort of girl who would make Janine wrinkle her elegant Parisienne nose and cross the street, he reflected with a quirk of amusement.

A blast of synthesised guitar music ripped through the summer night. Piet shook his head impatiently—he really was going to *have* to do something about this; it was just downright inconsiderate. Pausing to shrug his wide shoulders into the jacket of his formal grey business suit—although on such a warm night he didn't really need it—he let himself out of the apartment, and, scorning the lift, he strode briskly down the steep, narrow stairs to the street.

'Ouch! That stings!'

Charlie laughed. 'Well, you should have been more careful, Duncan. Fancy picking up broken glass with your fingers—there's a dustpan and brush some-where. Now hold still while I dab some more TCP on it.'

The handsome young man winced as she treated the cut on his thumb. 'I'm sorry, Charlie—that was your favourite vase. I'll buy you a new one tomorrow.'

'Oh, it doesn't matter.' Her pansy-blue eyes were smiling. 'There, clumsy. The bleeding's stopped—I don't think you'll need stitches.'

He slipped his free arm around her shoulders, and kissed the end of her pretty nose. 'Thanks—you're an angel. Come and have a dance with me now.'

She gave him a look that was meant to be stern. 'You're supposed to be going out with Sara,' she scolded him. 'Why aren't you dancing with her?'

'Oh, Sara's getting much too serious,' he grumbled petulantly. 'She's starting to hear wedding bells, and I'm not ready for all that yet—I still want to have fun. And you're the girl I'd most like to have fun with,' he added, tickling her. 'You're one person who really knows how to enjoy herself.'

'Maybe,' she countered, pushing him firmly away. 'But there's fun, and fun—and I don't think your idea of it is quite the same as mine.'

He laughed. 'Didn't your stuffy old father ever tell you about the birds and the bees?' he teased. 'You're a beautiful flower, and you're supposed to let the bees come buzzing around, sipping up your nectar...'

'Oh, am I?' she returned with dry humour. 'Well, if any bees come buzzing too close to me they might find out that I'm a Venus Fly Trap! Anyway, that music's much too loud. We really ought to turn it down—it's gone midnight.'

'Oh, it'll be all right,' insisted Duncan carelessly. 'It's only boring old banks and things along here— no one'll take any notice of us.'

'Even so. You know we aren't even supposed to be moored here. It's all very well for you, but it's my name on the lease, and I'll be the one who gets into trouble.'

'Oh, all right,' he conceded grudgingly. 'If you insist. Bossy-boots.'

She flashed him her sparkling smile. He always called her bossy-boots when she insisted on something—which wasn't very often. Sometimes she wondered if people didn't take too much advantage of her easygoing nature. It had seemed like fun at first when she had announced that she was going to go to Amsterdam instead of finishing her course at art school, and a bunch of her friends had decided to tag along. But after six months, with none of them worrying too much about earning any money or keeping the boat clean and tidy, she was beginning to get just a little bit fed up with it.

Oh, well—what did it matter? Better get rid of that glass, before someone else cut themselves. Finding the dustpan and brush, she swept it all up carefully, and took it up on deck to toss it into the canal. Then she stood for a moment, gazing around. It was a lovely warm evening; the sky was a deep velvet blue, spangled with stars. How could she be discontented on an evening like this?

And yet... Some part of her was beginning to grow weary of this rootless, Bohemian existence. It was all very well, living on a houseboat, throwing endless parties, but... it would be nice to be able to enjoy a little security for a change...

Laughing at herself, she shook her head. Her father would just love to hear her talking like that! Security, respectability—those were his watchwords. Not that he had ever offered much to her, his only daughter— he had never had the time. As a senior civil servant with the European Commission, he was a very busy man—as he frequently reminded her.

She was about to turn back down to the cabin when she noticed that someone had knocked over one of her favourite begonias. A cross little frown creased her smooth brow—that was just typical. Of course, it was an accident, but they might at least have had the decency to come and tell her. She stooped to pick it up, patting the compost back into place... and found herself unexpectedly at close quarters with a pair of very expensive handmade black brogues.

'Are you the owner of this boat?'

The brusque voice warned of a man who was accustomed to having everyone jump at his command, and she rose cautiously to her feet, her eyes travelling slowly up over an immaculately cut grey business suit, a conservative dark blue silk tie, to the hard line of a jaw that confirmed the impression of the voice.

'I said, are you the owner of this boat?' he repeated tersely.

'Well, yes—sort of,' she admitted, her voice a little unsteady.

'Then kindly turn that music down—at once. Don't you kids have any thought for other people?'

She might have apologised, explaining that that was exactly what she had been intending to do, but his tone instantly needled her, and she glared up at him in angry defiance. 'Why should we?' she retorted. 'No one's complained. No one lives around here, anyway—it's all offices.'

'I live around here,' he responded drily. 'Up there.' He indicated the windows of his apartment, up on the fourth floor of the tall, patrician building that housed the offices of Den Ouden Enterprises.

'Well, I'm sorry,' she countered, her mocking tone denying the apology in her words. 'How was I supposed to know that?'

'I'm telling you now. And I expect that music to be turned down to a respectable volume, and kept down.'

Charlie studied him warily from beneath her lashes. He was rather younger than on first impression she had assumed, though he must still be in his middle thirties. And he was very good-looking; dark blond hair, worn just a fraction longer than she would have expected, fell over a high, intelligent forehead, and his eyes were a cool grey.

But it was his mouth that fascinated her. How could such a beautiful, sensual mouth be so firmly controlled? What was he holding in check? A small *frisson* of heat ran through her. If ever that iron will-power unleashed its constraint the effect could be devastating!

He seemed almost amused by her scrutiny, conceding a flicker of a smile. 'Well?' he enquired.

Some demon of mischief had awoken inside her. 'Well . . . As you're the only one who's complaining,' she taunted saucily, moving towards him with a provocative sway, 'why don't you stay and join the party?' As she came close to him she had to tip her head back—he was over six feet tall, and she wasn't wearing any shoes. Playfully she twitched his expensive silk tie. 'Don't be an old fuddy-duddy.'

'Fuddy-duddy?' He looked quite surprised, and she concealed a small smile of triumph. He hadn't liked that one. But the next minute his hands slid around her waist, and he drew her hard against him. 'Very well, then, I will stay—if you will dance with me,' he challenged.

Charlie felt a sharp thud of panic. She was supposed to be the one running the game—she always was. But this tall stranger had turned the tables on her, and she wasn't quite sure what to do. The sheer impact of being held against that hard, muscular body, of breathing that subtle, heady muskiness of his skin made her heart beat just a little too fast.

She tried to draw back, but he wouldn't let her go. 'Don't tell me *you're* going to be a fuddy-duddy and refuse to dance with me until we've been formally introduced?' he teased, his eyes mocking her.

'No...I...' What was happening? How could she let some boring old businessman in a suit unnerve her like this? 'Of course I'll dance with you,' she retorted, her defiance as much for her own benefit as his. 'Are you sure you can dance to this sort of music?'

'Oh, I can dance to anything,' he assured her, the wicked gleam in his eyes conveying layers of unspoken meaning. 'Though I must say I'd prefer something a little more...romantic.' He had bent his head, and his breath was warming her ear, sending tiny little shivers scudding right through her.

Grimly she focused her attention on his tie, struggling to overcome the strange urge to let herself melt in his arms. A *tie*, for goodness' sake! The only man she knew who wore a tie was her father. Clinging to that image, she lifted her eyes again to his face.

'Why don't you take this off, then?' she suggested, tugging at the offending item. 'Or will your head fall off if you do?'

He smiled again—a smile that made her heart skid. 'You dislike my tie?' he enquired teasingly.

She shrugged one slim shoulder in a gesture that was supposed to indicate the most supreme indifference. 'Oh, not that one in particular. Just ties in general,' she returned, as cheekily as she would have liked to speak to her father. 'Only middle-aged people wear ties.'

'Is that so?' He appeared quite unruffled by her attempts to needle him. 'Well, in that case I must certainly take it off.'

He put up his hand and drew down the knot, still holding her close as she tried to draw back. Her mouth had gone suddenly dry. The act of removing his tie had conjured up a vivid image in her mind, as if he was going to start taking off the rest of his clothes...

'Better?' he taunted, his eyes glinting.

She couldn't answer. He had unfastened the top button of his shirt, and at the base of his throat she could see a cluster of rough light brown curls against the smooth bronze of his skin. Her throat felt parched—some deep, primeval instinct, as old as Eve, had caught her in its snare, and she didn't know how to regain control.

'Well, then, are you going to tell me your name?' he asked, his soft, smoky voice part of the spell that was weaving around her.

'It's...Charlie,' she managed, unable to quite suppress the slight tremor in her voice.

'Charlie.' The way he said it sent an odd little chill of heat scudding down her spine. 'Is that short for Charlotte?'

'Yes.'

'It's a very pretty name. It seems a pity to shorten it to something so masculine.'

'It doesn't shorten to much else,' she pointed out with a quirk of dry humour. 'Only Lottie.'

He laughed at that—a low, throaty chuckle that was disconcertingly sexy. 'Yes—I suppose perhaps it would be better to settle for Charlie,' he conceded. 'And so you own this boat, then, Charlie?'

It took a conscious effort to stop herself starting to like him; but the only defence she knew was the brittle shell of youthful insolence she used on her father. 'Do you mean, have I a nice, neat little set of title deeds, all signed up by a solicitor?' she taunted, as scornful as she dared. 'Of course not.'

' "Property is theft"?' he quoted, amused.

'Yes. Well, no,' she conceded. 'I rent it.'

'And all the others I've seen hanging around?' he enquired.

She shrugged again. 'They're . . . friends.'

'They don't live on this boat?'

'Some of them do. It's . . . rather a floating population.'

It was a rather thin joke, and he smiled drily. 'I see,' he murmured, those grey eyes glinting with sardonic humour. 'And is one of them your boyfriend, then, Charlie?'

A tinge of pink was colouring her cheeks, and she was glad of the evening shadows to hide it. 'Not particularly,' she returned, trying to sound casually dismissive. 'We don't believe in exclusive relationships.' That was a line that had almost given her father apoplexy. 'They're so stifling. To be truly creative you have to be free, to be open to every new experience.'

'Oh, I'm sure you're right. Nothing is more important than to be free.'

Was he mocking her? Covertly she studied his face from beneath her lashes, but she didn't know how to interpret that odd expression. What was she doing, anyway, dancing with a man in a *suit*? If her father could only see her now! He would certainly approve. Surely that was reason enough to dump this creep in the canal and go back to her friends, her own kind?

But somehow she seemed to have no will of her own. And as he slowly let his hand slide down over the length of her spine, holding her very, very close, she didn't object. He was moving her to the music, swaying gently, making the heavy guitar riffs of Whitesnake seem as smooth and romantic as Frank

Sinatra. Unconsciously she had closed her eyes, letting herself drift into the world he was creating.

And as his hand slid through her hair she tilted her face up to his, her heart fluttering like a trapped bird. His head bent slowly towards hers, and her lips parted softly, as if in obedience to some unspoken command. She knew, long before their mouths met, that this kiss would be something very special.

And it was. His sensuous tongue swirled languorously over the sweet inner membranes of her lips, stirring a response inside her that she had never known before. Fleetingly her mind registered a shock of surprise at his sheer expertise, so unexpected in someone who looked so formal and stuffy. But all rational thought was swiftly evaporating in the burning heat he was generating in her blood.

They had moved into some other dimension of time and space. Charlie was utterly lost—she didn't want it ever to end. She was responding helplessly, kissing him back, her slender body curved into his hard embrace as they danced slowly to the music. She wasn't even aware that he had danced her along the narrow gunwale of the boat, to the dark privacy of the space just behind the pointed bow. Here the sound of the loud rock music, the voices of her friends were more muted; instead there was the gentle lap of water against the hull, the whisper of the leaves of the tall elms that lined the canal.

Somehow she had come to slide her arms around his waist, inside his jacket, and was resting her cheek against the hard wall of his chest. The warmth of his body was permeating through her, and the subtle male muskiness of his skin was filling her senses. Nothing else seemed to matter any more. She had forgotten that he was older than any boyfriend she had ever had, that he wore a suit and polished shoes. She was aware only of the man, and of the disturbing sense of vulnerability he had made her feel. And all she wanted to do was dance in his arms, forever and ever.

The stars circled slowly above them as they let the music move them, kissing and holding each other as if they could never get their fill. At some point they stopped bothering to even pretend to dance and found a place to lean against the cabin of the boat, totally absorbed in their own intimate world, to the exclusion of all else.

Charlie had had lots of boyfriends—casual student relationships, never anything serious—and perhaps her fun-loving nature had led many of them to believe that she was 'easy', too. But they had soon learned their mistake. And yet tonight all her defences seemed to be asleep—somehow he had slipped past them, undetected...

At long, long last he lifted his head, a quirk of faintly sardonic humour in his smile. 'Well,' he murmured, his voice low and smoky, 'I'm glad I decided to stay.'

Charlie blinked up at him, suddenly alarmed as reality flooded back to her. He hadn't let her go—he was still holding her indecently close—and something in the dark gleam in his eyes warned her that maybe he had thought her invitation to the party had extended to rather more than a dance and a kiss.

She tried to step back, but with just the slightest hardening of his steel muscles he drew her even closer, his smile faintly mocking. 'But where are you going?' he taunted. 'You promised to dance with me.'

'I...'

'And you surely aren't afraid of new experiences?' he persisted, his warm breath fanning her cheek as he began to move her to the music again, slowly, sensuously. 'You who so much wish to be free.'

'This isn't a new experience for me,' she tossed back at him in breathless defiance. 'I've kissed dozens of boys...'

'Ah—boys.' He nodded wisely. 'But I think perhaps you have made the mistake of substituting quantity for quality.' He brushed his thumb sensuously over the trembling softness of her lips. 'You should not waste your kisses on mere boys. You are a woman who needs a man to kiss you—you could not be satisfied with anything less.'

His words, his voice were spinning a spell around her. The moon was shining on the dark waters of the canal, and a soft breeze stirred in her hair. Why had it never occurred to her before that Amsterdam was the most romantic city on earth?

His head bent as his mouth captured hers again, parting her lips in hungry demand, seeking all the sweetness deep within in a deliberately flagrant exploration that undermined all her will to resist. She put up her hand against his chest, her fingertips encountering the hard wall of muscle, and a thrill scudded through her, almost stopping her heart.

He sensed her response at once; of course he did—a man so experienced as this in the arts of making love would miss nothing. He curved her supple body against his, his kiss becoming deeper and more tender, sweeter than anything she had ever known, and she clung to him, yielding all that he demanded and more. She had no thought of the unspoken messages her wanton response was conveying—she knew only the depths of her own desire.

His hands were roving over her body with a sure possessiveness, making himself familiar with every curve. She had thrown a silky fringed shawl—bought in the street market for a few guilders—around her shoulders, catching it together with an old *diamanté* brooch, but somehow the pin had come loose, and she felt the shawl slip away.

She had worn it because the fine gauzy cotton thing she had on underneath was a little too low at the front, exposing rather more of the soft swell of her breasts than she cared to show. But now, with eyes that seemed to burn her tender flesh, he was enjoying the full benefit of the display.

She was so slender that she rarely bothered with a bra, and through the thin stuff of her top it was almost as if she were naked. Beneath his gaze she could feel the tender buds of her nipples harden to ripe peaks, visible beneath the cobwebby gauze. And as he touched her her breath caught in her throat.

If the cabin of the boat hadn't been there to support her she would have melted to the ground. She leaned back against it helplessly as he bent his head to swirl his tongue sensuously into the delicate whorl of her ear, and his palms flattened over her aching breasts, crushing them deliciously, rolling over the tender nipples with a heated friction that started a fever in her blood.

Her head tipped back, and a sobbing sigh escaped her lips. She heard him laugh, a low growl of triumph, and his mouth returned to claim hers again, as if it was his by right. She could only submit. She had no defences against the plundering invasion of his tongue, and her small breasts seemed to swell and ripen beneath the exquisite caress of his hands, betraying to him every nuance of her response.

'This is really not the place to continue this,' he murmured, his voice low and husky with sensuous promise. 'My house is only a step away, and upstairs I have a very large double bed, where we could be very comfortable.'

His words sliced through the dream she had been drifting into, and she opened her eyes in a shock of alarm. 'No!'

'No?' He frowned swiftly, puzzled by her seemingly capricious refusal. 'What game is this?' he demanded in growing anger. 'Is it that you are just a tease, after all? Promising all, and giving nothing?'

'Please ... I'm sorry.' She tried to pull away from him, startled by the dark intent in his eyes. 'Please let me go.'

'Maybe you have grown a little too sure of yourself, with only baby-faced children to handle,' he growled, savagely fierce. 'Perhaps it is time that you learned a small lesson about playing with the grown-ups.'

'No...please...I'm sorry...' Suddenly she was really frightened of him. He was still fully in control of himself; this was a very deliberate anger, and somehow all the more menacing for that.

His fingers laced tightly into her hair, dragging back her head so that her body was curved in a painful arc, hard against his. 'You should try to be a little more wise,' he snarled, his face very close above hers. 'Did your mother not warn you against playing with fire? It can be very dangerous—you could get badly burned.'

He pushed her back against the cabin, pinning her there with the weight of his body, and there was no escaping the hard mouth that crushed down on hers. She squirmed wildly, pounding at his solid chest with her fists, but, with every inch of her body crushed so intimately against his, every movement risked arousing him further. And he was strong beneath that formally tailored suit—devastatingly strong. She didn't stand a chance against him.

And oh, it would be so easy to surrender; she wanted him, wanted to spend the night with him in that big, comfortable bed; wanted to feel the live warmth of his naked skin against hers. Her body was beyond her control, yielding to him, supplicant...

He let her go so abruptly that she almost stumbled, banging her elbow painfully against the frame of the cabin. Those cold grey eyes lashed over her in chilling distaste. 'On second thoughts, I have no wish to dirty my sheets with goods that have probably been picked over and sampled by half the men in Amsterdam,' he sneered, his voice laced with contempt. 'Go back to your trivial young boys. For myself, I prefer to be a little more discriminating.'

And, turning on his heel, he mounted the pavement with one swift step, and vanished into the darkness beyond the tall, elegant elms that lined the canal. She watched him go, tears of shame choking her throat. It was her own fault—she had given him every reason to believe that she was the sort of girl who would go to bed with a total stranger.

A brief flare of light and a passing silhouette showed as he opened the door of his building and closed it behind him. With an effort of will Charlie pulled herself together, and, picking up her fallen shawl, pinned it neatly back into place.

Anyway, why should she care what he thought of her? She had never liked that sort anyway. Hadn't her father tried to introduce her to enough of them, boring young business executives and budding politicians, pleading with her to 'settle down' with someone respectable?

Well, she didn't want to settle down, and she didn't want to be respectable. And she didn't like men who wore suits.

CHAPTER TWO

THE floating flower market beside the Singel was always one of Charlie's favourite places to paint. The daffodils and tulips of springtime had given way now to roses—roses of every variety and hue, banks of them, arranged in great bucketfuls, surrounded by clouds of delicate white gypsophila. The bright canopies of the barges along the canal-side sheltered them from the harshest light of the sun, bathing them in a subtle glow of golden yellow.

It was impossible to capture every detail on canvas; and, anyway, that wasn't the way she liked to paint. She liked to use colour to create an almost fluid impression of what she could see, the vision of her mind rather than the vision of her eyes.

She had propped her bicycle against the wall, and set up her stool and easel well back on the pavement to create as little obstruction as possible for the crowds that flowed around her. Several passers-by had already stopped to admire her work, and she accepted their flattering comments with a smile, secretly amused that the ones who peered too closely to see anything but a mass of bright splodges were usually the ones most fulsome in their praise.

The pretty carillon bells of the Munt tower had just chimed out the half-hour, and she was beginning to think of taking a short break for coffee, when some strange sixth sense made the small hairs on the back of her neck start to prickle. She tried not to look

round, but her will-power just wasn't strong enough
to overcome a force stronger than gravity itself.

Her instincts had been right—it was him. He was
standing some five feet behind her, studying the
painting on her easel. He was wearing an expensively
tailored grey suit again, the uniform of the highly successful businessman, which no doubt he was. And
yet . . . somehow the image didn't quite seem to fit.

Oh, the suit fitted—quite superbly, moulding his
wide shoulders to perfection. But there was something . . . maybe it was in the way he moved . . . Suddenly her mouth felt dry, and she found herself
remembering much too vividly the way it had felt to
dance in his arms.

It was almost a week since she had seen him, but
she hadn't been able to get him out of her mind. At
first she had kept out of sight, almost afraid of
bumping into him, but then her self-respect had re-
asserted itself, and she had been angry, wanting only
an opportunity to tear him off a strip for the insulting
way he had treated her. But, as the days had passed
without even a glimpse of him, an aching longing had
settled into her heart.

And now here he was, calmly strolling towards her,
smiling as if she was no more than a chance-met
acquaintance. She stiffened in bristling defensiveness,
turning away from him to fiddle with a mix of saffron
and cadmium on her palette.

'That's very good,' he remarked, nodding towards
the easel, sounding faintly surprised, as if he hadn't
expected her to have a talent for anything.

'Thank you.'

'How long have you been painting?' he persisted, amused to know that she would have preferred to ignore him.

She lifted one shoulder in a casual shrug, indifferent whether he stayed or not. 'Oh, years—since I was about fifteen or sixteen.'

He nodded seriously. 'Ah—many years, then.'

Her eyes flashed him an angry glare, recognising that he was mocking her. Did he think she was a child? 'I'm twenty-two,' she informed him with dignity.

He lifted one quizzical eyebrow. 'Are you really? You don't look it.'

'Well, I am.' She knew she didn't look her age. It was her hair, today bunched up on top of her head and tied with pink and yellow ribbons. She could never make it look elegant, no matter what she did with it—it was just too curly.

He came closer, and bent to examine the painting. She tried to lean away from him, precariously close to overbalancing on her low stool—but she didn't want to breathe the musky male scent of his skin, feel the warmth of his body within inches of hers.

'You have a very mature technique,' he commented with the perception of one who knew what he was talking about. 'You have studied at art college?'

'Yes—but I dropped out,' she responded, a hint of belligerence in her voice. 'I didn't want to be a graphic designer, or work in advertising.'

'No.' Again that mocking seriousness. 'So, do you sell your paintings?'

'Of course not,' she informed him with lofty disdain. 'If people genuinely like them I give them away. There are more important things in life than making money.' She cast a fleeting glance of contempt at his slim leather briefcase—it had always been a rule of thumb of her father's that the slimmer the briefcase, the more important the executive.

He smiled, clearly understanding her message. 'So, how do you afford to eat?' he enquired, deceptively mild.

'I have an allowance from my father...' Even as she said it, the irony of it struck her, and she felt a tinge of pink begin to colour her cheeks.

'Ah. How very convenient.' There was a ruthless edge of sarcasm in his voice. 'You are able to live off your father, and have no need to sully your hands with crass financial considerations, as other people do.'

'Yes... well... I don't take all of it,' she muttered, furious with herself, and furious with him for making her feel so embarrassed. Impatiently she began to pack her painting materials back into the wooden box she carried them in.

His manner changed unexpectedly. 'You're not going?' he asked, a note of apology in his tone. 'Please, not on my account. You haven't finished your painting.'

'I'm going to have a coffee,' she snapped, determined not to let him guess the profound effect he had on her.

'Then let me buy it for you,' he offered at once.

'No, thank you.'

He smiled wryly. 'You are very angry with me—as you have every right to be. I'm afraid I rather lost my temper the other night, and my behaviour was less than gentlemanly. I would have come down much sooner to apologise, but I have been away on business. Please accept my apologies now.'

She stared up at him warily. He *seemed* to be quite sincere—at least she could detect no trace of mockery in his eyes. Turning back to her painting box, she shrugged one slim shoulder. 'Apology accepted,' she responded flippantly. 'It was no big deal—you don't have to buy me a coffee to make up for it.'

'But I would like to,' he persisted, unperturbed by her street-hardened manner.

She looked up at him again, puzzled. 'Why?' she demanded baldly.

A glint of sardonic humour lit those cool blue-grey eyes. 'Why not?' he countered on a light note of teasing. 'I have spent most of the past week at a series of very tedious business conferences, with a lot of very boring old fuddy-duddies, and it would be very pleasant to relax for a short while in the company of a pretty girl.'

And then what? she wanted to ask. It took little imagination to guess what was in his mind. The memory of his invitation, that night on the boat, to share his big comfortable bed came back to her like a warning voice. For her own safety, she ought to back away from him right now.

And yet... it was so tempting to take the opportunity to spend just a little time with him. It would only be for half an hour, after all. What harm could there possibly be in that?

As she hesitated, uncertain, he simply took her silence for assent and picked up her paint-box. 'Oh... it's OK, we don't have to take that,' she told him, her voice just a shade unsteady. 'If I leave my things here against the wall the stall-holder will keep an eye on them for me.'

He nodded, and helped her stack her painting and easel neatly out of the way of passers-by. The café where she usually had coffee was near by, and he followed her down the three steep steps, ducking his head under the low lintel of the door.

The café was very traditionally Dutch, with brown wood-panelled walls and simple wooden tables and chairs. On the threshold Charlie hesitated again, wishing she had thought not to bring him here. It was a popular meeting-place among the crowds of young people who flocked Amsterdam, and the contrast of their casual Bohemian clothes with his formal business-suit highlighted uncomfortably that he was a representative of very different world from the one in which she belonged.

Several people had already glanced up and seen her, and greeted her with waves and smiles. She cast a cautious glance up at the man at her side. 'Shall we . . . go somewhere else?' she suggested hurriedly. 'It's a little crowded in here.'

'No, it isn't,' he argued, apparently quite untroubled by looking so out of place. 'Come, there's a table over there.'

He took her arm, steering her across to the far side of the room, away from the high counter where most of the customers were gathered, drinking coffee or beer and playing dice. Usually she would have resented such high-handed treatment, but his touch sent such a flame of heat through her that she couldn't quite think straight.

She found herself seated at the table he had chosen, and from the corner of her eye she could see Karin, a student from Utrecht who was spending her summer vacation working as a waitress, moving in fast. Karin had a kind of radar for attractive men, and would certainly not let a small thing like a crisply knotted silk tie put her off.

'Charlie—hi!' The greeting was warm, but the girl's attention was all on the impression she was creating on the handsome stranger—how *did* she get into jeans so tight? 'Hello,' she purred, angling for an introduction.

Charlie felt a sudden twinge of embarrassment. She had danced with this man, so close that she knew the beat of his heart; she had kissed him, had almost been tempted to make love with him, but she didn't even know his name. He smiled across the table, swiftly understanding her problem. 'It's Piet,' he supplied.

'Ah . . . yes. Karin—Piet,' she managed shakily.

'Hello, Piet. What can I get you?' Karin was playing the efficient waitress, but her smile hinted invitingly that that wasn't the only service she might be prepared to provide.

'Just two coffees, please.'

'With cream?'

'Black for me,' he responded, only the glint of sardonic humour in his eyes conveying that he was fully aware of the girl's blatant flirtation. He must get that kind of thing all the time, reflected Charlie wryly. It was really small wonder that he was inclined to be a little arrogant.

He had leaned back in his seat, regarding her with the look that she found so disconcerting—she was never quite sure if he was mocking her. 'Well, then, Charlie—it seems you have a great many friends in Amsterdam,' he remarked lightly.

'Yes, I suppose I have.'

'You have lived here long?'

'Oh, about six months. We had the boat round on the Muidergracht, but we—er—kept getting complaints about the noise. I'm sorry about the other night,' she added with a slightly sheepish smile. 'Sometimes it gets a bit...wild.'

He laughed softly. 'But if it hadn't been noisy,' he returned on a faint hint of teasing, 'I would have had no excuse to come down and complain, would I?'

She slanted him a swift, wary glance from beneath her lashes—it was disconcerting the way he never responded quite how she expected him to. She lifted one shoulder in that careless, characteristic shrug. 'Oh, you could have come down anyway if you had wanted to,' she managed, struggling to maintain her cool façade. 'Anyone can drop in—we don't hand out printed invitations.'

He nodded thoughtfully. 'Ah, yes—a very commendable generosity. And so this group of you live together in happy conviviality?'

'Yes.' Why was it that she felt as though he was filing away her answers?

'And there are no quarrels between you? No boy-girl jealousies? Ah—but of course,' he added, a dry edge of cynicism in his voice, 'you do not believe in exclusive relationships, do you?'

Had she really said that? She must have been trying hard to behave even more outrageously than usual! Well, she certainly wasn't going to deny it now—though it wasn't easy to maintain her flippant manner when he was looking at her like that. 'Of course not,' she declared. 'Who does, these days?'

'Many young women would prefer a little more stability in their lives,' he pointed out mildly.

'Huh! What an old-fashioned attitude,' she countered dismissively. 'Besides, no one expects a man to be looking for stability—the more girls he can sleep with, the better. Why should it be different for a woman?'

'And is that what you prefer, Charlie? The freedom to indulge in casual sex with whomsoever takes your fancy?'

'Of course.' She could feel a blush of pink rising to her cheeks again, but she slammed on recklessly, 'What's the alternative—to have one man see me as his exclusive property, to wash his socks and cook his dinner, and tell him the earth moves every time he makes love to me? No, thank you.'

She was beginning to wish that the floor would open up into a deep pit and swallow her. Why was she talking like this, pretending to be something she was not? Why did she want him to think so badly of her? Perhaps it was a kind of defence. The worse he thought of her, the less likely he was to want to pursue their relationship any further. But what was he thinking, sitting there watching her so levelly, giving nothing away? He made her feel as if he could see right into her soul, and know that she was lying.

Fortunately at that moment Karin came back with their coffee, providing a very useful distraction as she set the cups down on the table, brushing a little too closely to Piet as she did so. 'Will there be anything else?' she asked, her voice deliberately adding layers of meaning to the line.

Piet shook his head. 'Thank you—not just at the moment,' he responded, a dry note of humour in his voice.

'Well. I'll...see you later, then.' She slanted him a meaningful smile, letting it linger over her shoulder as she moved away to serve someone else, her slim rear end in those skin-tight jeans swaying in a way that provoked a gleam of appreciation even in Piet's cool grey eyes.

Charlie bit back the surge of jealousy that rose inside her, and laughed, assuming an air of worldly sophistication. 'You see what I mean?' she challenged. 'It's the old double standard. You say you disapprove of my behaviour, but I bet you'd jump into bed with Karin like a shot.'

He shook his head, his eyes deadly serious as they held hers. 'You mistake me,' he said softly. 'I neither approve nor disapprove of your behaviour. It is entirely your own concern. It is merely that, for myself, I find no pleasure in casual sex.'

Charlie felt her cheeks flame scarlet—that had certainly put her in her place. But after all, hadn't she set out to earn his contempt? So why did she feel like crying? Picking up her coffee, she took a sip, hoping he wouldn't notice that her hand was shaking. Why had she let herself be tempted into having coffee with him in the first place? She should have kept ignoring him, and eventually he would have gone away.

He too was sipping his coffee, and she could feel his eyes resting on her, keeping her in a state of acute tension. But when at last he spoke again it was to completely change the subject. 'So, Charlie, why did you choose to come and live in Amsterdam?' he enquired in a conversational tone.

Relieved at being able to talk about something neutral, she responded readily. 'Oh, because it's lively, because I can paint here. It's such a lovely city, with the canals and all the beautiful old houses. There's nowhere else quite like it.'

'You paint always in oils?'

'Oh, no—just when it seems right for the subject. I do water-colours sometimes, and acrylics. And sometimes I do murals. I did one at a shopping centre in Hilversum a couple of months ago,' she added with pride.

He lifted one eyebrow in quizzical amusement. 'A commission?'

'Yes.' She conceded a wry smile. 'I do take them, now and then.'

'Ah.' He nodded slowly. 'Then perhaps, if I may come down to your boat some time and see your work, I may have a commission for you,' he suggested.

'Oh?' Her heart thudded in alarm.

'In my offices. There is a rather dull wall in the reception area that would benefit from a little colour—something lively and modern. Would you consider it?'

She hesitated, searching for some excuse to refuse, but with those cool grey eyes resting on her like that her brain refused to function. 'M . . . maybe,' she stumbled. 'I'll see . . . if I have time.'

He smiled, knowing full well that she had all the time in the world—she wasn't doing anything else. He seemed quite relaxed, apparently unaffected by the charge of static electricity that seemed to tingle in the air between them. 'Tell me, then,' he went on easily, 'where do you come from, Charlie?'

'Oh, everywhere and nowhere.' She couldn't quite erase the trace of bitterness from her voice. 'I was born in Hampshire, but my father works for the EC Commission, and he's always on the move. So I grew up in boarding-schools.'

'What about your mother?'

'Oh, she cleared out when I was five.' She made a casual gesture with her hand; this little speech was so much a part of her armoury that she could deliver it without feeling any of the pain. 'I can't say I blame her—she must have been just about ready to die of boredom.'

'She abandoned you?' His tone clearly conveyed his disapproval.

'No, she didn't, as a matter of fact,' she tossed back at him, glad to be able to set him straight on one thing, at least. 'She took me with her. We went to live in a commune in Wales. It was great. Three years I lived there—and then my dear father decided she wasn't a fit mother for me, and went to court to get custody of me. I don't know why he bothered—*he* didn't want me. What use is an eight-year-old, tagging around? He couldn't wait to bundle me away to a nice respectable boarding-school, where they could teach me to behave like a young lady. Only they never succeeded,' she added with grim satisfaction. 'None of them did.'

'And what happened to your mother?' he asked.

'She died.' The unexpected gentleness of his voice suddenly brought the tears frighteningly close to the surface. 'A couple of years after I was taken away. She was living in an old caravan, and the heater in it was faulty. Carbon-monoxide poisoning, in her sleep.'

'I see. I'm very sorry.'

Charlie looked away from him. Why on earth had she told him the truth? Her usual version of the story was simply that her mother had run away to a hippy commune, leaving her behind. How had he made her lower her hard-won defences like that?

Piet smiled, those grey eyes still serious. 'It is understandable, perhaps, that you should feel such animosity towards your father,' he mused. 'But it is a pity that you should choose to make the worst of your own life, simply to punish him.'

She blinked at him, unnerved by the accuracy of his perception. She should have been more careful; she had been letting him in far too close. What else might he guess about her? Struggling desperately to revive her flippant front, she shrugged in casual unconcern.

'I've already been psychoanalysed, thank you— several times. I'm so bad that I must be mad, right? It's nothing new.'

He conceded a nod. 'My apologies,' he murmured, an inflexion of sardonic humour in his voice.

'Anyway,' she countered brashly, 'I've given you my potted life-story. So what's yours? Come on—let's have a little equality here—my turn to analyse you.'

'Oh, my life has been fairly uncomplicated.' He spoke casually enough, but there was a guarded note in his voice that alerted her attention. 'My father inherited a small business from his father, and worked hard all his life to build it up. When he died my brother Rutger took it over, and when he died—he was a number of years older than me—it passed into my hands.'

Charlie regarded him covertly from beneath her lashes. He had spoken of his brother's death in such a matter-of-fact tone, but she sensed that he wasn't as unaffected by it as he pretended to be. 'Your brother can't have been all that old,' she remarked, probing carefully.

'He was thirty-five.' He pulled a wry face. 'The same age as I am now.'

'How did he die?' she asked, unconscious of the softening of the expression in her blue eyes. 'Was it an accident?'

He shook his head. 'A heart attack,' he said. 'Overwork.'

'Oh.' Impulsively she leaned across the table, and laid her hand on his. 'I'm sorry. You must have been very close to him.'

Just for a moment he left his hand with hers, but then he withdrew it, leaning back in his seat. 'Not really,' he dismissed briskly. 'There were ten years between us. And we had very different interests. In fact, we had very little in common.'

He had retreated from her, his tone indicating quite clearly that he didn't wish to discuss the matter any further. She felt a tug of regret; once again he was the cool, distant businessman in a suit. And, finishing his coffee, he glanced at his watch.

'I regret that I must go now,' he said, picking up his briefcase as he rose to his feet. 'Thank you for a most pleasant interlude.' He held out his hand to her in polite formality. 'Goodbye.'

She hesitated, and then briefly she placed her fingers in his, withdrawing them quickly before he could notice how they trembled. 'Goodbye.' She had to struggle for control of her voice. 'See you around.'

'Quite possibly.' He smiled. 'Perhaps I might come down to your boat one afternoon, and you will show me your paintings?'

She shrugged, trying for an air of nonchalance. 'Of course. Any time.'

'And perhaps then we may discuss the matter of this mural I wish to commission?'

'Sure. Just tell me what you want.'

'Thank you. Well, goodbye, then.'

'Goodbye.' She didn't watch him go—she was afraid that, if by chance he should look back, she would give away too much.

What was happening to her? It was crazy—she couldn't control her emotions, she couldn't keep him out of her mind. She had never reacted like this to any man she had met before.

Of course, most of the men she had gone out with had been her fellow art students, the same age as her, the sort who shrugged off the tedium and responsibilities of everyday life to pursue elusive dreams— though most of them would eventually sell out their ideals and settle down to work for advertising agencies and glossy magazines, she acknowledged drily.

To be honest, part of their attraction had always been that they horrified her father, with their long hair and scruffy clothes, and outspoken—if somewhat garbled—anarchistic opinions. But the sort that *he* wanted her to go out with, smart and clean and successful, had never appealed to her.

So what made Piet so different? Of course, he was very good-looking. And those well cut suits did nothing to disguise the hard, muscular maleness of his body. And that evocative muskiness of his skin stirred all sorts of strange physical responses inside her...

Her mouth felt suddenly dry, and she gulped down the rest of her coffee quickly. There it was again— the racing heartbeat, the dizzy light-headedness. Just thinking about him could make her go hot all over—

and she seemed to be thinking about him nearly all the time.

But what was *he* thinking? He seemed to despise her—and yet he had deliberately sought her company. If he had only wanted to apologise he needn't have offered to buy her coffee. And why had he spoken about wanting her to paint a mural for him?

A smile of bitter cynicism twisted her soft mouth. Wasn't it obvious? In spite of what he had said, like most men he couldn't resist the lure of a girl who seemed to offer an easy conquest with no strings attached. Well, he would soon find out his mistake, she vowed fiercely. Oh, she would let him go on thinking she *was* that kind of girl—only not with him. That would take him down a notch or two.

'Well, that was what I call *gorgeous*!' Karin sidled into the seat that Piet had just vacated, her eyes alight with excitement. 'Where did you meet him?'

Charlie shrugged. She didn't really want to tell Karin anything, but she knew she would persist. 'Oh...he lives in one of the buildings down on the Heren, next to where we've got the boat,' she explained briefly. 'He came down to complain about the noise one night, and...well, we sort of got talking.'

'You don't mean the Den Ouden building?' asked Karin eagerly.

Charlie looked at her, faintly puzzled by the question. 'Well, yes, as a matter of fact. I suppose he's got an apartment upstairs or something.'

'Charlie, don't you realise who he is? That's *Piet den Ouden*!' Karin's emphasis told Charlie that the name should mean something, but she looked at her friend blankly. 'I thought I recognised him, but I couldn't believe it. You seemed to be awfully friendly with him,' she added, probing with little subtlety. 'Are you going to be seeing him again?'

Charlie shrugged with casual unconcern. 'I doubt it,' she responded. 'Who is he, anyway—apart from owning Den Ouden's?'

'Isn't that enough?' demanded Karin. 'It's one of the biggest companies in Europe. And, besides, he used to be a champion stock-car racer. My brother practically worshipped him. Just wait till I tell him I've actually met him!'

'Stock-cars?' queried Charlie, frowning. That didn't quite fit with the image she had of him.

'Oh, it was a long time ago now,' Karin told her breezily. 'He retired—I can't remember why. It was very sudden—no one was expecting it.'

'His brother died,' murmured Charlie, putting two and two together. 'He had to take over the family business.'

'Oh, was that what it was?' Karin picked up the empty coffee-cups and rose to her feet. 'Anyway, I'll see you tonight—Duncan said you're having another party,' she added as Charlie looked faintly surprised.

'Did he? Well, in that case we probably are,' she conceded with wry resignation.

CHAPTER THREE

'JUST look at those damn kids! Somebody ought to do something about it. That boat's an eyesore, and I wouldn't mind betting there are drugs and all sorts of things going on down there.'

Piet barely looked up from the contract he was studying as Dirk van Leiden, one of his most important suppliers, paused in his irritating pacing around the room to look out of the window. 'Yes, Dirk, I'm sure you're right,' he murmured neutrally—he had no wish to get drawn into a discussion about the psychedelic houseboat and its occupants. They had proved far too much of a distraction already.

Why had he allowed himself to spend so much time with that girl this afternoon? He had intended to pause only briefly, no more than good manners allowed—after all, he acknowledged uncomfortably, he did owe her an apology. His behaviour last week had surprised him; certainly she was a provoking little baggage, but there could be no justification for the way he had so nearly allowed himself to lose control.

But somehow he had found himself offering to buy her a coffee, and then staying so long with her that he had been late for an important appointment. He had even found himself fabricating an excuse to see her again. He had no intention of permitting her to paint one of her murals in the tastefully refined offices of Den Ouden's—nothing could be more out of place.

And, besides, he didn't want any of her work about the place, constantly reminding him of her...

Damn, she was doing it again—sneaking into his mind, just when he needed all his concentration. How did she do it? There was no denying, of course, that she was exceedingly pretty, but that didn't really explain it—he had dated any number of pretty girls over the years. Maybe it was that intriguing combination of street-wise worldliness with an almost childlike vulnerability...

But a girl like that had no place in his orderly life, he reminded himself firmly. He had to do something to take his mind off her—perhaps he should take Janine out to dinner. Now she *was* a beautiful girl, always so elegantly dressed, the sort of girl any man would feel proud to have on his arm.

Reaching decisively across his desk, he flicked the switch on the intercom to his secretary. 'Lenneke, get Mademoiselle de Savary on the line for me, will you?' he requested in a crisp tone.

'Yes, *meneer.*'

Lenneke sounded faintly surprised, and Janine probably would be too—he wasn't due to see her until Saturday. But never mind—a small break from routine would do him good.

'What do you think, Piet?' Dirk was persisting.

Piet glanced up at him questioningly—he had lost the thread of the other man's conversation some time ago.

'We should get the police to come and clear that boat away. I'm sure they wouldn't have to look too hard to find a reason—the thing's probably awash with drugs.'

Piet shrugged his wide shoulders. 'You are probably right,' he conceded in a bored tone. 'I would be more than happy to see them removed from my front door.'

'I'll get on to the commissariat,' Dirk asserted briskly. 'Mind you,' he added, leaning closer to the window, a sudden lascivious interest in his voice, 'that's a cute little piece of tail, that blonde one. I wouldn't mind tying her down for a closer look.'

'What on earth's going on in here?' Charlie stared around the small rear cabin of the houseboat in horror. A dozen people were crowded into it, mostly sitting on the floor, and she would have had to be a complete idiot not to realise what they were doing.

One of the long-haired freaks on the floor—a hanger-on who had trailed across from England with the art-school crowd—slanted her a bleary-eyed look. 'Hey, what are you so uptight about, Charlie-baby?' he drawled languidly. 'There's no harm in it. Why don't you come and try some. It's the best kick there is.'

'It looks it,' she retorted sarcastically, casting a disparaging eye over the pallid, vacuous faces gazing blankly up her. 'Get out of here, right now. Or I'll call the police.'

He laughed, not believing she was serious. 'Oh, relax,' he coaxed thickly. 'It's just a little angel-dust——'

'I know what it is,' she snapped. 'I mean it, Stu. I'm not having drug-taking on my boat.'

'Oh, come on, Charlie.' He reached for her hand, trying to pull her down into his lap. 'Don't be a spoilsport.'

She tugged her hand free. 'How long has this been going on?' she demanded furiously. 'You know I hate drugs.'

'Well, you're the one who's always saying I should get a job,' he argued, his voice slurred. 'I've got a nice little business here.'

'You mean you're *supplying* this stuff?' She stared at him in horror. There was an old tobacco tin on the floor, with a plastic bag full of white powder inside. She stooped and picked it up. 'Stuart, there's enough in here to send half of Amsterdam on a trip!'

He giggled. 'I've got a friend with a chemistry set!'

'Well, you're not selling it on my boat,' she insisted firmly. 'If you're not out of here by the time I count three this little lot goes straight in the canal. And if you ever show your face around here again I *will* call the police.'

There was a howl of protest from the floor. 'Charlie! Hey, come on, baby, there's no need to——'

Suddenly there was a noise from the deck above them, a stampede of heavy feet coming down into the cabin. 'The police!' yelled someone, and pandemonium broke out. People were pushing and shoving to get out of the door, and Charlie found herself knocked to the floor. In the midst of all the shouting, half a dozen burly policemen had erupted into the cabin and were seizing people, dragging them away.

Charlie flinched into a corner, trying to keep out of it, but suddenly a giant in a police uniform loomed over her, and she felt a hard grip on her arm. 'Wait,' she gasped as she was unceremoniously hauled to her feet. 'I'm not——'

'Who's the owner of this boat?'

'Well, I am, but...'

She was still clutching the tin that had held the drugs in her hand, and the policeman spotted it. 'What's this?' he demanded, his fist closing over hers so that she couldn't drop the incriminating evidence. 'Jaap, over here.'

'No, please—you don't understand...' she protested as another officer came over to witness what the first had found.

But neither of them was in the mood to sit down and discuss it. 'Come on,' they ordered impatiently, and hustled her out of the door.

She gasped at the scene of chaos outside. There were half a dozen police cars, and two patrol boats, their sirens blaring, their blue lights flashing into the night. People were running every which way, and several scuffles had broken out as some tried to escape arrest. Over by the rail, she saw Duncan fighting with a policeman twice his size.

'Duncan!' she cried, her voice rising in panic. 'Stop it—don't be stupid. You'll only make things worse.'

Desperately she tried to pull herself away from the policeman who was holding her, and at that moment someone barged into him, enough for him to loose his grip a little, and she darted away quickly, grabbing at Duncan and pulling him back.

Somehow they all went down on the deck together, in a mêlée of arms and legs. Someone had a knee on her back, holding her down, and she screamed, trying to struggle free. By the time she was hauled to her feet Duncan was in handcuffs, and she was gasping for breath, her hair all tumbled around her face.

This time the policemen weren't going to let her go. Two of them hauled her across the deck and up the sloping gangplank to the pavement. She tried to protest, to tell them she wasn't resisting arrest, but she couldn't get the words out.

A small crowd had gathered, watching with interest. She felt her cheeks scarlet with shame as she realised that her hair was all over the place, her dress dirty and torn. Bundled without ceremony into the back of a police car, she pushed the hair back from her eyes, brushing away the tears that were soaking her cheeks.

A light, high up on the fourth floor of the Den Ouden building, caught her eye. A dark silhouette stood motionless at the window, looking down. Piet. What was he thinking, standing there so still? He must have seen what had happened. Well, it would certainly have confirmed his impression of her.

As she looked up, a second figure appeared—unmistakably a woman. The two shapes merged, and then moved away from the window. That was the last she saw as the police car pulled away.

'*Piet's* offered to stand bail for me?' Charlie stared at her solicitor in surprise.

The solicitor nodded. 'Meneer Den Ouden.' There was a distinct trace of feminine susceptibility behind that briskly efficient exterior. 'A most charming man—and eminently respectable, of course. I'm quite sure the Commissar d'Instruction will accept a surety from him. That is, if you're really determined not to call your father...?'

'No,' insisted Charlie forcefully, shaking her head. 'I'd rather stay in prison.'

'Well,' the solicitor pointed out with dry logic, 'I'm afraid that will be your only option, unless you accept Meneer Den Ouden's offer. These so-called ''designer'' drugs are a very serious problem, you know, and the police are determined to stamp them out.'

'It wasn't mine,' Charlie felt compelled to re-inforce, although she had already made a long statement. 'I wouldn't touch drugs—of any sort. Never.'

The solicitor smiled wryly. 'For what it's worth, I believe you,' she said. 'But it isn't me you have to convince. And it may be quite a long time before the case comes to court.'

Charlie hesitated, twisting her hands together nervously. Two nights in the accommodation offered at the ugly modern police headquarters on the Elandsgracht had been quite enough. She would do almost anything to get out—anything except ask her father for help.

Oh, he wouldn't refuse, of course—he wouldn't want anyone to suspect that he was anything but a good, caring father who didn't deserve a daughter who brought him so much trouble. Arrested on *drugs* charges now! She could almost hear his measured, reproaching voice.

'But why would Piet offer to stand bail for me?' she mused aloud.

'I understand from his call that he has commissioned you to paint a mural for him,' the solicitor said. 'Is that not correct?'

Charlie blinked in bewilderment. 'Well, I . . . Yes, it is,' she agreed quickly. Of the three options open to her, that seemed marginally the least unpleasant—and, after all, if he was prepared to make the offer . . .

'Good.' The solicitor closed her notebook with a brisk little snap, and rose to her feet. 'The bail hearing is set for tomorrow morning. I doubt if the public prosecutor will contest it if we can offer so respectable a surety as Meneer Den Ouden. Good afternoon, Miss Heller.'

The hearing, in the Commissar d'Instruction's chambers, was quite brief. Charlie sat with her head bowed, unable to meet Piet's eyes. What must he be thinking of her now? She hadn't liked to think too hard about why he had offered to stand bail for her. What was he hoping to get out of it?

But, whatever ulterior motives he might have, it felt wonderful at last to be out in the open air. She couldn't restrain herself. Throwing her arms wide as if to embrace the whole world, she executed a few little dance steps in the street. 'Ah, freedom—glorious freedom!'

'Quite,' Piet remarked dampeningly. 'Shall we go to my car, or do you propose to dance all the way home?'

She slanted him a cautious look from beneath her lashes. He didn't seem angry with her, precisely, but he clearly wasn't too pleased, either. Well, she really shouldn't be surprised at that, she acknowledged wryly. And she had to be grateful to him for getting her out of the dismal prospect of an indeterminate spell in custody, awaiting trial, that had confronted her.

'Your car,' she conceded, walking with a little more decorum.

He nodded, and led the way to a sleek bronze Mercedes parked beside the canal. He opened the passenger door for her, and she slid into the well upholstered leather seat with a comfortable sigh.

'This is a bit of a change for you, isn't it?' she remarked as he slid in behind the wheel.

He slanted her a raised eyebrow.

'From stock-car racing, I mean.'

A certain tension in the line of his hard jaw warned
her that it was a subject he didn't like to talk about.
'That was a long time ago,' he returned dismissively.

'You never told me about it,' she persisted, determined somehow to get beyond that brick wall he had
built around himself.

'It's no longer relevant.'

'Do you miss it?' she asked, still bold.

He chose not to respond—a very effective way of
silencing her.

It was only a short distance to the Herengracht, but
the morning traffic was heavy in the narrow one-way
streets that ran along the banks of the canals through
the old centre of the city. Charlie was always fascinated by the tangle of trucks and cars, trams and bicycles—it seemed incredible that anyone ever got
anywhere.

But when they finally turned on to the Herengracht
she was in for a shock. The houseboat was being tied
up to a barge, ready to be towed away. 'What's happening?' she demanded, scrambling out of the car.
'What are they doing with my boat?'

'It would appear that they are removing it,' responded Piet, an inflexion of sardonic humour in his
voice. 'And not before time.'

She stared up at him, aghast. 'But . . . it's my home!
Where am I supposed to go?'

'For the time being, you will be staying in my
apartment, naturally.'

A deep rush of pink coloured her cheeks. 'Stay with you? But... I can't do that!' she protested, her voice unsteady.

'It is a condition of your bail,' he reminded her evenly.

'Well, yes, but... I didn't think you intended to keep me to it,' she argued, not quite able to meet his eyes.

'Of course that was what I intended,' he responded in that uncompromising tone. 'I would not have said that I did if I didn't.'

'But you can't want me staying with you,' she pleaded in growing panic. 'I'll... be in your way.'

'Quite probably,' he agreed, unsmiling. 'But nevertheless that is what we both agreed to do. If you have changed your mind you may, of course, return to the commissariat and submit to custody.'

She slanted a wary glance up at him from beneath her lashes. There was no doubting that he meant exactly what he said. 'That doesn't give me much of a choice, does it?' she grumbled bleakly.

'I regret I cannot offer a wider range of options.'

'But what about all my things from the boat?' she asked.

'I imagine it will be possible for you to arrange to collect them before they tow it away,' he suggested. 'You may bring them up to my apartment.'

Charlie sighed, conceding defeat. 'Thank you,' she mumbled reluctantly.

'Will you require any assistance?'

'Well... there are quite a few bulky things to carry,' she admitted. 'My easels, and my canvases.'

'I will instruct my secretary to send one of the staff down to you,' he said. 'Lenneke will also show you around the apartment, and will deal with anything else you may need.'

With a brief nod he turned away, leaving her staring after him in a mixture of surprise and bewilderment. He had made it abundantly plain that, although he had come to her rescue, he had no time to spend with her. Well, that was probably just as well, she reflected wryly. If she was going to have to live in his apartment the less they saw of each other, the better!

It didn't take her very long to pack her clothes, but her painting gear was a longer job. There were two easels—the little collapsible one she took with her when she went out, and a bigger one that stayed up permanently. Then there were her canvases—she had amassed a couple of dozen in the time she had been in Amsterdam, in all shapes and sizes that made them awkward to carry.

She had to smile to herself when two fresh-faced young men from Piet's office came to the gangplank, calling out tentatively, their eyes nearly on stalks with curiosity about what they had been asked to do. They must be leaping to all sorts of conclusions, she guessed with a quirk of wry humour.

'Ah, can you take these?—thank you,' she requested breezily, pulling out some of the canvases, so that they found themselves staring at a half-finished life-study of Sara, as naked as the *Venus de Milo*.

They both nearly choked. 'Y...yes, miss,' they nodded, glancing at each other, red-cheeked, as their speculation received confirmation.

What would Piet make of that picture? she wondered mischievously. Maybe she should leave it casually around somewhere where he would be bound to see it—would that be enough to penetrate that armoured reserve of his? And it was going to drive him mad, having her things cluttering up his neat apartment; she knew before she had ever seen it that it would be neat, all modern design and polished smooth.

Wistfully she looked around at the cosy little cabin of the houseboat. Of course, if she was absolutely honest she would have to admit that it wasn't particularly convenient. But it was so bright and charming, with its old wooden furniture, designed to make the most of every last inch of space, and its jumbled cotton prints on curtains and upholstery, which would have clashed dreadfully if they hadn't all faded gently together into a kind of harmony.

And then there were her plants. She had cultivated them all so carefully, taking cuttings from all over the place; they were almost as important to her as her paintings. She couldn't possibly leave them behind. Well, Piet hadn't said she couldn't bring them too, she reminded herself, chuckling. But he probably wouldn't be too pleased.

The windows of the Den Ouden building were lined with faces, which vanished instantly as Charlie stepped up out of the cabin and then reappeared discreetly, all craning to peer down at her. Piet was going to take a very long time to live this down, she reflected with grim satisfaction.

A crisply efficient woman, of what the French called 'a certain age', was waiting at a door next to the office to admit her. Charlie smiled a little uncertainly. 'Thank you,' she offered. 'I hope you weren't terribly busy?'

'Not at all,' the woman assured her—though Charlie guessed that the answer would have been the same whatever. She held out her hand. 'I am Lenneke. Please will you come this way?'

Charlie followed her into a small private hallway, very stark with its plain white-textured walls and discreet recessed spotlights. A small lift took them up to the fourth floor, where there was another similar hall, and, taking a key, she opened a door, standing aside to invite Charlie to step inside.

She had been right about the apartment, she mused, gazing around. Sleek and spare, just as she had guessed it would be. One long room ran along the front of three of the tall narrow buildings; a gleaming floor of pale beech, and white-textured walls, made a cool backdrop to just a few items of very expensive, very stylish furniture. Open-plan, it had a space for working, a space for dining, and a space for sitting; ivory slats of vertical louvre blinds covered the windows, and the only ornamentation was a stark modern sculpture of twisted black metal.

'The guest suite is through here,' Lenneke stated, leading the way across the room. Behind the main frontage of the buildings each had an annexe; most of the houses in the centre of Amsterdam were built that way, to provide the maximum of space within the narrow width. Charlie found herself in a very comfortable bedroom, with its own dressing-room and luxury bathroom.

'I hope this will be satisfactory,' Lenneke said. 'If you require anything the telephone is here beside the bed. To reach me you simply dial one—if you need an outside line, dial nine. I will leave you now to settle in.'

'Thank you.' Charlie smiled again. 'I'll try not to make a nuisance of myself.'

A little to her surprise, the secretary smiled back warmly. 'Oh, I don't suppose you could do that,' she said. 'It'll be nice to have you here, brightening the place up.'

'Thank you,' responded Charlie, smiling in delight at the unexpected friendliness. 'Well, I'd better let you get back to your proper work, or Piet will be annoyed.'

Lenneke shook her head. 'He isn't difficult to work for,' she insisted gently. 'His bark's a great deal worse than his bite.'

That thought remained with Charlie as she wearily gazed around at her things, which the two young men had brought up for her. It was going to take her a long time to put them all away. But first she needed a shower—though she had been able to wash and change at the police station, its antiseptic smell still seemed to linger on her clothes.

The bathroom in the suite was quite something— all glossy black tiles and gold taps. Thankfully she stripped off her clothes and stepped under the shower. The warm needles of water were soothing, drenching down through her hair and running over the slender contours of her body. There was a bottle of luxurious *crème* soap on the shelf, and she poured a generous slurp of it into her palm, running her hands down over her soft skin.

He had caressed her, that night on the boat, his hands so skilled and sensitive, stirring all sorts of unfamiliar responses in her. The memory was so vivid that she could almost feel the imprint of his touch. She had never let any of her art-school boyfriends take such liberties, but with him . . .

He *did* want her; he must want her, to have kissed her like that. And even now, though he was out-

wardly so cool, she could sometimes catch that glint
in his eyes, an unmistakable clue. And why else had
he stood bail for her, when he could have just ignored
her, needn't have got involved at all?

She stepped out of the shower and took a big fluffy
towel, scrubbing herself vigorously dry. And then she
stood gazing critically at her own reflection, naked,
in the large, well lit mirror above the sink, trying to
imagine what Piet would have thought if he could have
seen her.

Was she too thin? Her breasts were so small, her
hips almost boyish—would he prefer a more mature,
womanly shape? Turning her back and twisting to peer
over her shoulder, she examined the soft curve of her
derrière—her best feature, or so Duncan had told her
several times...

Impatiently she shook her head. What was she
doing, allowing herself to think like this? Everyone
on his staff was certainly assuming that she was his
new mistress, installed up here in his private
apartment. Was he assuming the same? Until she had
a clearer idea of his intentions she would be wise to
exercise a little caution.

Quickly she wrapped a towel around herself,
clutching it tightly with one hand, and, opening the
door, stepped out into the bedroom—and found Piet
standing there, idly glancing through some of the
canvases stacked against the wall.

'What the...? What are you doing in here?' she
demanded, breathless with shock. 'Don't you believe
in knocking?'

'I did knock,' he responded evenly. 'There was no
reply. I assumed that you had gone out.'

'Oh...' She noticed that he had been looking through the stack that contained the painting of Sara. Suddenly it seemed rather childish and silly to think he might have been shocked by it. He wouldn't be shocked—he must have seen all that and more, many times before.

'I was wondering if perhaps you might be so good as to place some of your belongings a little more tidily,' he requested with exaggerated politeness. 'At present my living-room has the appearance of an obstacle course.'

She glanced through the door into the main room. He had every reason to complain, she acknowledged fairly—the pristine apartment looked as if it had been the scene of a riot. 'I'm sorry,' she responded wryly. 'I'll try and find a home for everything. The only trouble is my plants.' She looked up at him appealingly. 'They need to be near the light, and there's not nearly enough space on the window-sills in here.'

'Then some of them may remain in the living-room,' he allowed.

'Thank you.' It unnerved her, the way he stood there watching her—she could feel her skin prickling with heat. And it didn't help that he could appear so cool all the time. What did it take to get through to him? She slanted him a provocative glance from beneath her lashes. 'It's very kind of you to let me stay here,' she murmured, her voice deliberately soft. 'Aren't you afraid I might steal your valuables or something?'

'Not at all,' he responded, unruffled. 'I will arrange for Lenneke to give you a key. There is one thing, however, that I must insist upon. Please do not trespass on my good nature by bringing any of your boyfriends into my apartment.'

Triumph! 'Jealous?' she taunted, mocking him as much as she dared.

He smiled drily. 'I do not think so. May I have your promise that you will abide by my stipulation?'

Charlie laughed, too delighted to discover that he wasn't as immune as he was pretending to be to notice the warning glint in his eyes. 'You *are* jealous,' she insisted, moving unconsciously towards him. 'You just want to get me into bed yourself!'

He shook his head. 'Let us have one thing absolutely clear between us,' he stated, his intonation very precise. 'I have no intention of abusing the position you find yourself in. You may rest assured of that.'

But all she could think of was how he had caressed her, how he had kissed her. All she wanted was to feel his arms around her again. 'But you *do* want me,' she pleaded, her eyes misty as they gazed up into his. 'I know you do.'

Just for one beautiful moment she thought he was going to admit it. But then he drew back, his eyes cold with contempt as they flickered down over her. 'Thank you for the generous offer,' he sneered in icy sarcasm. 'However, I am afraid I must decline. That which is so freely available has never held much attraction for me.'

With a shock of horror she realised that the hand holding the towel around her body had slipped, uncovering the rounded swell of her small breasts, still glowing from the warmth of her shower, the rosebud tips pertly inviting. A rush of shame coloured her cheeks deep pink.

'You think I'd go to bed with you?' she threw at him, humiliation kindling her fury. 'You're practically old enough to be my father!'

He smiled, maddeningly arrogant. 'Not quite,' he demurred. 'But you are rather too young to interest me. And, as I said, too available. Maybe when you are older you will learn a little more sophistication, a little more mystery, to intrigue a man. But at present you are no more than a pretty trifle who would bore me long before morning.'

As he turned and calmly walked towards the door the rage inside her exploded. The nearest thing to her hand flew across the room, missing him by wildly aimed inches. He slanted her a look of sardonic humour, and glanced down at the mess she had made on his highly polished floor.

'How unfortunate,' he taunted. 'One of your precious plants. Still, perhaps all is not lost—you may yet be able to place it back in its pot. I shall see you this evening—I shall be dining out, but you may make your own arrangements.'

He was gone, closing the door behind him, leaving Charlie shaking and close to tears. No one—*no one*—had ever spoken to her like that before. But she had deserved it, she acknowledged bitterly. She had given him every reason to have a low opinion of her. She only had herself to blame if he thought she was a slut.

CHAPTER FOUR

WHY did people get drunk for pleasure? Charlie closed her eyes briefly, but her head still seemed to be revolving unpleasantly. The discothèque was noisy and hot—why had she even come? She never enjoyed herself here.

'Hey, Charlie! Come and dance with me.' She closed her eyes again—Duncan was really a little too much to take in her present state. But he hauled her ruthlessly to her feet. 'Come on, we've got to celebrate our freedom. I really thought we were both going to get it this time.'

'Where's Sara?' she protested, stumbling as her head swam.

'Oh, she's gone off with some geezer from Dusseldorf,' he snorted with exaggerated contempt. 'I suppose she thinks she can make me jealous.'

Charlie squinted up at him a little blearily. 'You know, it would serve you right if she ditched you,' she warned him. 'You're always going off with other girls.'

He laughed, trying for an air of unconcern. 'Oh, she knows it doesn't really *mean* anything,' he insisted.

'Does she?'

'Of course she does. I wouldn't *seriously* get involved with anyone else—I love Sara.'

'Have you ever told her that?'

He grinned sheepishly. 'Well, no,' he admitted. 'But why else does she think I've stayed with her all this

59

time? I've never stayed with one girl for so long before. Anyway, come on,' he added, uncomfortable with the subject. 'It's far too hot in here for dancing. Let's get another drink.'

'No.' She pulled back as he tried to draw her through the crowded disco. 'I've had a bit too much already. Anyway, I'd better be going,' she added wryly. 'It's pretty late, and Piet'll be hopping mad if I disturb him.'

'Oh, all right,' Duncan conceded reluctantly. 'I'll take you home, then.'

She tried to shake her head, but found it made her even dizzier. 'Oh, no, it's all right,' she protested. 'I'll be OK.'

'No, I'd better,' he insisted, uncharacteristically gallant. 'Can't have you wandering the streets in that state.'

She didn't argue. She was uncomfortably aware that she had recklessly overdone it, and she didn't want to end up falling into a canal on the way home. Duncan was really the lesser of the two evils.

The fresh air hit her like a punch from a heavyweight boxer, sending her reeling on the ropes. Duncan caught her arm, supporting her. 'Maybe we'd better get a taxi,' he suggested. 'It's after midnight—the trams have stopped running.'

'No, I'd rather walk,' she insisted. 'It might sober me up a bit. Anyway, it isn't far.'

They set off together in a rolling gait—Duncan wasn't exactly sober either. Charlie was beginning to seriously regret what she had done. She hadn't intended to stay out so late. She had left the apartment before Piet had come back up from his office, and had gone down to one of her regular haunts to meet her friends and find out what she could about what had happened to those who had been arrested.

She had only stayed out to avoid spending any time alone in the apartment with Piet. The idea of going home slightly tipsy had come later, out of a rebellious desire to prove that she didn't give a damn how badly he thought of her. But she had misjudged the amount of alcohol required—probably because she rarely drank at all.

They had turned on to the Herengracht when a sleek bronze Mercedes purred past them, turning to park nose-on to the canal outside the Der Ouder building. 'That's him!' hissed Charlie, so surprised to see him returning so late that she missed her footing and swayed off the kerb, her arms flailing as she recovered her balance.

Duncan caught her by the waist, and before she had time to realise what was happening he had swung her into a darkened doorway, trapping her there with the weight of his body. 'You're drunk,' he declared un-necessarily. 'I've never seen you so drunk before.'

'Duncan . . .' She didn't quite like the way he was holding her, and tried to push him away. 'Let me go—I'd better go in.'

'You can stay out a little while longer,' he argued, his beer-soaked breath almost asphyxiating her. 'He's only just come home—he won't be in bed yet.'

She tried to twist away as his mouth came down to find hers. 'Duncan, stop it,' she protested, trying to push him away. 'What about Sara?'

'Never mind Sara,' he argued, fumbling to get a proper hold on her. 'She's not here.'

'Duncan——'

'Pardon me for interrupting.' That ice-cool voice seemed to be descending from a great height. 'I saw you walking along the road. If you have finished saying goodnight, perhaps you are ready to come inside?'

In a mixture of relief and humiliation Charlie pushed Duncan away, tugging her disordered clothing straight. 'Yes, I'm coming,' she mumbled, not quite able to look up at him. 'Goodnight, Duncan.'

He grunted something incoherent, and stalked away.

Piet walked calmly over to his door and put the key in the lock. 'I regret that I could not permit you to invite the young gentleman in to spend the night,' he said. 'You did accept that as part of our agreement.'

She slanted him a belligerent look from beneath her lashes. 'I hope you don't think I'm going to spend the night with *you*,' she sneered—rather ruining the effect by tripping over the doorstep.

He laughed in mocking contempt. 'I assure you, in your present condition there is absolutely no possibility of that,' he informed her. 'I have no taste for drunken women. Quite apart from the unpleasant aroma of stale alcohol, they have an unfortunate tendency to respond like a sack of potatoes.'

She glared at him, unable to think of a sufficiently biting response. Instead she felt a sudden alarming wave of nausea grip her. 'I think I'm going to be sick,' she muttered.

And she was, violently. Somewhere in the depths of her misery she was aware of Piet, supporting her patiently, soothing her with his soft voice, stroking back her hair. 'I'm sorry,' she kept mumbling over and over. 'I'm so sorry.'

'It's all right,' he assured her with unexpected sympathy. 'You're not the only person in the world who ever had too much to drink.'

'I shouldn't have—I didn't mean to. You're so kind. Thank you.' She let herself lean against his wide chest, wallowing in the sheer happiness of feeling the warmth of his strong arms around her.

'I think perhaps you should go to bed now, if you feel a little better?' he suggested, his voice gentle.

'Yes, please,' she whispered humbly.

He almost had to carry her up the stairs and into the apartment. The dazzle as he turned on the lights was painful for her eyes, and she closed them tightly, leaning weakly against him. With a soft laugh he picked her up and carried her over to her bedroom, as easily as if she weighed nothing at all...

Charlie woke with a thick head, and a dozen emotions in her heart—shame and guilt at the memory of what had happened last night, relief that her hangover wasn't as bad as she deserved. And then shock, as she realised that beneath the bedclothes she was naked, except for the skimpiest pair of white lace briefs.

She had no recollection of what had happened after Piet had laid her down on the bed—she had blacked out. She certainly hadn't removed her clothes herself. So Piet must have done it. A fine shimmer of heat ran through her. He had done no more than remove her clothes, she knew that—his words of last night still burned in her brain. But the thought that he had seen her virtually naked...

With a low moan she rolled over and buried her face in the pillow. She didn't want ever to get out of bed—she didn't want to face him. How could she ever look him in the eye again? It was bad enough being sick all over his shoes ... !

A sharp rap on the door froze her. She kept her eyes closed, desperately hoping that he would think she was asleep and go away. But she heard him open the door, heard his footsteps coming over to the bed. He didn't speak, and in the silence she felt herself growing increasingly uncomfortable. He wouldn't be fooled by her act—he would know she was awake.

Slowly she let herself feign a return to consciousness, shifting her position and then opening her eyes with a show of reluctance, apparently surprised to find herself in a strange room, taking a second or two to recognise the tall man standing beside her bed.

'Oh ... hello,' she managed, yawning. 'What time is it?'

'Almost lunchtime,' he responded. 'I have brought you a glass of orange juice—a moderately good remedy for a hangover, I believe.'

'I haven't got a hangover.' And she couldn't imagine that he had ever had one, either.

'You're extremely fortunate, then.'

Was that a glimmer of a smile? 'I'm very sorry about last night,' she managed, her cheeks a delicate shade of pink. 'Did I make an awful mess?'

'Nothing that couldn't be cleaned up.'

'Thank you for the orange juice.' She reached her arm out from beneath the covers and picked up the glass. The juice was freshly squeezed, deliciously sweet and refreshing; she could feel herself reviving with every sip. 'Mmm—that was lovely,' she sighed, handing him back the empty glass.

'I usually have something cold for lunch on a Saturday. Would you care to join me?'

'Th... thank you.' Why was he being so nice to her? She eyed him suspiciously. Nothing *had* happened last night, had it? No... She would have known...

'If you are wondering what has happened to the clothes you were wearing last night, I have thrown them away. They were... a little the worse for wear.'

'Thank you.' She could feel her cheeks beginning to colour with embarrassment, and hid it swiftly behind a brash façade. 'It was a bit of a surprise to wake up and find myself with only my drawers on. I was afraid I might have missed something interesting.'

A glint of sardonic humour lit his eyes. 'I assure you, if it had been interesting, you would not have missed it,' he countered, the husky tone of his voice underlining his point.

She half choked, wishing she could retreat—but there was nowhere to go except further on to the bed. Once again he had turned the tables on her, responding to her attempts to goad him with an answer that was completely unexpected.

There was a sympathetic acknowledgement of her confusion in his smile. 'Perhaps I had better leave you to get dressed,' he suggested. 'Lunch will be ready whenever you are.'

To her relief, he withdrew, leaving her alone. She scrambled out of bed, mentally sifting through her clothes to pick something that he might like. She didn't have a great selection to choose from—jeans mostly, and a few ethnic-print skirts, and a selection of T-shirts and cotton tops. Not the sort of thing that he would find attractive.

And yet... he *was* attracted to her, whether he cared to admit it or not. She couldn't forget the tender way

he had held her in his arms last night when she was
being so sick. A man who could be so patient, so tol-
erant was really *worth* something.

She sat down on the edge of the bed, her mind suddenly filled with a single thought. She loved him. He
was the solid rock her wild heart had been seeking
through all the storms of her life.

No, it was ridiculous, she argued, trying hard to be
rational about it. She couldn't possibly have fallen in
love with him. She didn't *like* that boring sort who
wore suits and ties all the time and thought about
nothing but business and responsibilities.

But Piet wasn't *boring*, she reminded herself, rolling
back on the bed and closing her eyes. Just thinking
about him could make her toes curl. It was in his eyes,
and in the way he smiled sometimes, creasing that tiny
line into the corner of his mouth. And in the hard,
muscular power of his wide shoulders, and the evocative male muskiness of his skin...

She sat up quickly, startled by the vivid images that
had come into her mind. She *must* be in love with
him—she had never even thought of doing things like
that with any other man before. But the problem was,
how did she get him to admit that he felt the same?

Bouncing off the bed, she scampered into the
bathroom for a quick wash, and then pulled on a pair
of figure-hugging jeans, the denim faded and soft so
that it moulded to her slim shape, and a T-shirt that
colourfully proclaimed her allegiance to the campaign to save the rainforests. She brushed her hair,
and tied a few twists of narrow ribbon in it to nestle
among the wild curls, and then regarded her reflection with satisfaction. That ice-blooded automaton

in the next room had better watch out—she was about
to blow his fuse!

The aroma of freshly brewed coffee was filling the
apartment, and Charlie felt her appetite stir. Piet was
in the kitchen, spreading thick *belegde broodjes* rolls
with jam. He glanced up as she came in, his eyes
briefly registering an interested reaction to her appearance before returning to his task.

She leaned across the breakfast bar, laughing teasingly. 'Goodness—he can even cook!'

He slanted her a look of restrained humour. 'I can
at least manage to fill a roll,' he responded drily.

'And make a mean cup of coffee, if that smell's
anything to go by.' She swung into the kitchen, looking
around in admiration. 'Mmm—neat. But aren't you
scared that if you touch the wrong button you'll
launch into hyper-space? ''Captain's log, Stardate
four-one-seven-nine-eight-point-two,''' she intoned,
her eyes dancing. '''Attacked by alien can-opener in
the outer galaxy of Nova Centuri. Beam me up,
Scotty.'''

Yes, he really could laugh. He didn't want to—there
was a distinct gleam of reluctance in his eyes as he
yielded—but even his iron will couldn't hold it in
check. And his laughter transformed his whole face,
lighting his eyes with warmth. She moved towards
him, utterly fascinated.

'You know, you should do that more often,' she
murmured, putting up one finger to trace the narrow
line that was creased into the side of his mouth.

His eyes glinted with sardonic amusement, and he
held out a well stuffed *belegd broodje*, putting it between them like a shield. 'Lunch,' he said, firmly dis-
missing her attempts at flirtation.

She pouted, but took the roll, and slipped up to perch on the high breakfast-bar, swinging her bare feet. Some wicked demon inside her was prompting her, and with deliberate intent she lifted one hand to flick back her hair, knowing that the movement would make her small breasts strain against the clinging fabric of her T-shirt.

Those intriguing sea-grey eyes regarded her steadily, refusing to register either approval or disapproval. 'Do you always go without a bra?' he enquired in a conversational tone.

'Mostly.' So he wasn't immune—he might pretend to be, but she could tell from the hard set of his mouth. But she hadn't expected to comment quite so bluntly. Maybe that was enough for now. It was one thing to tease him a little—it was quite another to goad him to the point of explosion.

'Coffee?' he enquired.

'Yes, please.'

'Cream and sugar?'

'Just a little cream.'

She felt a shiver of heat as he came close to hand her the mug of coffee, but at once he moved away again, to lean against the counter on the far side of the kitchen, a good, safe distance away.

'You didn't tell me where you were going last night,' he said.

She pouted crossly. Was he going to start laying down the law to her now? 'So what?' she retorted petulantly. 'You're not my father, you know.'

His mouth curved into a grim smile. 'No—I am certainly *not* your father,' he agreed. 'A deliverance for which I am profoundly grateful. However, I should remind you that I *am* responsible for you while you're on bail.'

She shrugged one slim shoulder in a gesture of unconcern. 'I wasn't going to do anything you'd disapprove of.'

He laughed drily. 'How do you know what I'd disapprove of?' he enquired, a trace of sardonic humour in his voice.

'Well, you wouldn't approve of me bringing friends up here, for one thing,' she countered, wishing she hadn't let herself get into this conversation—it was leading in entirely the wrong direction.

'I have no objection to you bringing *friends* up here,' he responded evenly. 'What I will not permit is that you bring young men up here. You may pursue your promiscuous lifestyle if you wish—but not in my apartment.'

She glared at him in angry defiance, biting back her immediate protest that she wasn't promiscuous. Let him go on thinking that if he wanted to. He probably wouldn't believe her if she denied it anyway. She slanted him a provocative glance from beneath her lashes.

'I know why you wouldn't like it,' she taunted him, the turmoil of her emotions throwing her completely off course. 'It's got nothing to do with trespassing on your good nature. You're just jealous because I'd rather go to bed with Duncan than with you!'

She had gone too far—she was regretting it as soon as the words were out of her mouth. It was as if she had lit a slow-burning fuse. Very deliberately he put down his coffee-cup, and crossed the room towards her, his eyes glinting with a dangerous intent.

'Oh, really?' he challenged softly. 'Strange—from my observations last night, it appeared to me that, drunk as you were, you weren't keen to even let the young man kiss you.'

Charlie shrank back instinctively, but she was trapped on the high kitchen counter. She flinched in shock as he grasped both her wrists, jerking her roughly towards him.

'And let there be no misunderstanding,' he grated, a hint of menace in his voice. 'If I *did* want you in my bed you would be there. Be in no doubt of that.'

His eyes were as stormy as the grey North Sea, and as she gazed up into them she felt as if she was drowning. And then with a muttered curse he dragged her into his arms, and she gasped in shock as his mouth came down on hers in a kiss of fierce intensity, crushing her lips apart.

His tongue plundered ruthlessly into the sweet softness of her mouth in a flagrantly sensual exploration, finding every deep, secret corner. Anger and arousal were warring inside him, both equally dangerous, and in an instinct of pure self-preservation she offered him only passive submission, letting him inflict on her what he would.

His hands were caressing her body with a rough possessiveness, and their mouths broke apart as they both dragged for breath. For a brief moment she thought that perhaps some sanity might return to him, but then he bent his head to trace a path of fierce, burning kisses into the delicate shell of her ear, and down into the sensitive hollows of her throat.

His fingers had tangled into her tumbled curls, tipping her head back, making her body a vulnerable arc, and her small breasts were strained against the cotton of her T-shirt, the ripe, hard buds of her nipples standing out pertly, invitingly. With a low growl he bent over them, taking one dainty fruit deep into his mouth, suckling it fiercely through the cotton.

A low moan of sheer erotic pleasure escaped her lips. She was losing her grip on reality—and it seemed that he was too. Whatever he had said just now, he wanted her—and for one wild moment she really thought he was going to take her, right here in the kitchen. And there wasn't going to be a thing she could do about it.

It was the sound of a key in the lock that broke them apart, breathless, staring at the door in shock as it swung open. Piet stepped quickly away from her, running a hand back through his tousled hair, and she tugged at her T-shirt, her cheeks flaming scarlet as she tried to hide that betraying patch of dampness over her breast.

'Piet?' The accent was French, the perfume expensive, the hair red and glossy, falling in stylishly coiffured waves around her shoulders. She turned, laughing, as she came through the door. 'I've been shopping, and I thought I would just drop in to leave my dress for this evening—it will be so much easier if I change here instead of going back to——' A perfect scarlet mouth opened in a gasp of surprise as she saw the freakish-looking girl perched on the breakfast-bar. 'Oh . . . !'

'Good afternoon, Janine.' Piet's wry greeting acknowledged the awkwardness of the situation. He stepped forward coolly, and welcomed her with a swift kiss on the cheek as he took a clutch of shopping bags, bearing the logos of the most exclusive shops in

Amsterdam, from her hand. 'This is Charlie,' he added succinctly.

'Charlie?' The girl's eyes turned from him to Charlie, transmitting icy suspicion.

Charlie conjured a wobbly smile.

'She will be staying here for a short while.'

'Staying *here*?'

'For a short while.' Even Piet knew that he was going to have a great deal of difficulty explaining this one. 'Come and sit down,' he said, taking the girl's elbow and guiding her over to the leather settee.

But she shook her arm free with an angry gesture. 'But who is she?' she demanded, slanting another hostile glare at Charlie. 'What's she doing here?'

'I will tell you, if you will sit down.'

Charlie slid down from the breakfast-bar. 'Don't mind me—I'm going out,' she announced brightly. 'Don't worry—I won't be late back.' Something in Piet's fixed expression awoke that demon inside her again. As she strolled over to the door she scooped up her pink nylon shoulder-bag and the brocade waistcoat she intended putting on over her T-shirt, and then with a provocative smile turned back to the couple on the settee. 'Bye, Piet,' she purred, and softly blew him a kiss.

She heard the start of the explosion as she closed the door behind her.

Charlie was nervous about returning to the apartment. It was her fault that Piet had quarrelled with his girl-friend. She wasn't sorry about that, but she couldn't expect him to be pleased. Had he managed to smooth things over? Her heart was thudding as she approached the door, and it wasn't from skipping up the three steep flights of stairs from the street.

Tact suggested to her that perhaps she should knock, instead of using her key. The door opened almost at once, as if he had been waiting for her. 'Good afternoon,' he greeted her with chilling formality. 'Nice of you to return.'

'Hello.' She managed a wry smile, glancing around the apartment—there was no sign of the French girl, or her shopping, and the scent of her perfume had faded. 'I'm sorry about what happened this afternoon,' she added awkwardly.

'Are you?' He flicked a cool glance over her, and turned away. 'You surprise me. I thought it was your intention to prove that that delectable little body is sufficiently irresistible to overcome any distaste I may feel at its free availability to all and sundry.'

She lanced him an angry glance, wasted on his unyielding back. 'That wasn't what I meant,' she protested. 'I meant...I'm sorry that I caused you to have a row with your girlfriend. I don't suppose she'd have been very pleased at finding me here, even if... what happened...' Her voice foundered in confusion.

'If what happened hadn't happened?' he queried drily. 'Quite possibly. In the event, she was quite understandably extremely upset. She has now left, and will not be returning.'

'Oh...' She lowered her eyes, gazing down at the disreputable canvas trainers on her feet, scuffing his highly polished floor. What was she to think? He sounded...irritated, but not particularly upset. 'I'm sorry...I didn't mean to break up your relationship,' she mumbled.

For a long moment he stared at her bowed head, and then he shrugged, and moved back to the large ash-wood drawing-board, where he had evidently been working. 'It was not a "relationship"—at least, not in the sense which I believe you mean. However, it has placed me in a somewhat difficult position. This evening I am due to attend a charity function, and Janine was to have accompanied me. It is now too late for me to contact anyone else to take her place.'

She lifted her head, studying him with wary caution. Since it was her fault that his girlfriend had left, she really ought to try to make amends in some way. But after what had happened, dared she offer...? 'Well, you...you could always take me instead,' she suggested diffidently.

'You?' He raised one sardonic eyebrow, regarding her with cool disdain. 'I hardly think it will be the sort of occasion you would enjoy—it will be very formal.'

'I know how to behave on formal occasions,' she protested, stung. 'I've often been to them with my father.' She turned on her most winning smile. 'I wouldn't let you down, I promise.'

He still looked doubtful. 'Have you anything suitable to wear?'

'Yes. Somewhere...' She pulled a wry face at the thought of the probable condition of her only evening dress, tucked away in the bottom of one of her suit-cases. 'I expect it'll need ironing, though.'

'That will be no problem.' He conceded a dry smile. 'Very well—it begins at eight, so we should leave in about an hour, if you can be ready by then?'

'Of course.'

'And I trust you *will* try to behave... with decorum,' he added, a shadow of doubt crossing his face. 'Some of the other guests will be people I do business with—politicians, bankers, industrialists. They tend, in the main, to be of a somewhat conservative nature, and can be easily shocked.'

'I'll be a saint,' she vowed solemnly—though inside she was already beginning to regret that she had ever made the suggestion. It didn't sound as if it was going to be much fun.

But at least it would give her an opportunity to give Piet a better impression of her, she reminded herself, her characteristic optimism swiftly returning. She really would do her very best to be exactly what he wanted her to be.

CHAPTER FIVE

CHARLIE studied her reflection in the mirror with a wry frown. Her father had bought this dress for her to wear to a dinner party at ten Downing Street, not trusting her to choose something suitable in which to be presented to the British prime minister.

It had been the most excruciatingly boring dinner party she had ever attended, tucked away near the bottom of the table away from all the more interesting people, forced to choose between pandering to the ego of some junior treasury minister and listening to a couple of desiccated civil servants discussing the price of fish. She hoped that wasn't going to prove an ill omen for tonight.

It was a lovely dress, granted, if you liked that sort of thing. Of midnight-blue satin, it had a clinging ruched bodice cut low across the curve of her breasts, with a matching bolero to lend it a respectable modesty. The skirt was slender, tapering to her ankles, with a small kick-pleat at the back to allow her to walk.

She had put her hair up into an elegant French pleat at the back of her head, drawing it firmly into place to try to suppress a little of its wild curl, and she had put on the neat gold stud earrings her father had bought her for her eighteenth birthday. Her make-up, though she was wearing slightly more than usual, was applied with a light hand—just a hint of navy blue mascara to highlight the blue of her eyes, and a gleam of raspberry gloss on her lips.

But she looked like a stranger; Charlotte—even Miss Heller. Not Charlie. The high heels of her evening sandals made her appear taller than usual, lending her an unfamiliar air of dignity and sophistication. Was Piet going to like it?

He was in the sitting-room when she opened the bedroom door, looking devastating and more than a little dangerous in a beautifully cut black dinner-jacket, with a handmade silk shirt and a bow tie that by some lucky chance was the exact match for her dress. Like some sleek urban panther, she thought wildly as he turned to survey her.

He didn't approve. What was wrong? Was it her hair? Did the dress cling a little too closely to her slender form? 'Isn't . . . isn't it what you wanted?' she queried, her voice unsteady.

'Oh, yes—it is most suitable.' There was just the faintest glint of sardonic humour in his eyes. 'I was a little taken by surprise, that is all—you look . . . so very different.'

'Oh. But you . . . don't like it?'

He smiled in swift reassurance. 'Indeed I do—you look very beautiful. Come, shall we go? The reception is in a building just on the other side of the canal, so I propose that we should walk—it seems really rather unnecessary to drive that short distance.'

'Of . . . of course.'

He opened the door, and she preceded him across the narrow carpeted hall to the private lift—in these sandals, she didn't fancy the idea of walking down three flights of steep stairs.

She still didn't feel quite sure whether he really liked the way she looked or not. That frigid formality of his always made her feel so uncomfortable. If only she could get closer to him, really understand what he was thinking. Maybe this evening—maybe if she tried very hard to please him, to behave exactly how he wanted her to behave, he would soften towards her a little.

To Charlie's surprise, the function was being held in the glittering showroom of one of Amsterdam's leading diamond houses, surrounded by millions of pounds' worth of the most beautiful gems in the world. But anyone harbouring nefarious ambitions would have been thwarted by the impeccable security.

At the door two large uniformed guards scrutinised everyone's invitations, before allowing them—no more than two at a time—to enter the first of a pair of glass doors. Charlie walked straight through the small vestibule, expecting the second door to open, but it remained firmly closed behind them.

'High-impact bullet-proof glass,' Piet informed her succinctly. 'And video cameras.'

She glanced up and saw the dark lens watching her from a corner of the ceiling, and guessed that at the same time they were being electronically scanned for concealed weapons. That mischievous imp inside her head was tempting her to poke her tongue out, but dignity prevailed. And evidently the faceless system was satisfied, permitting the second pair of doors to open to admit them to the showroom itself.

A white-coated waiter came forward promptly, offering them a silver tray bearing elegant tulip-shaped glasses of chilled champagne. Charlie sipped hers sparingly, gazing around with an interest she did not trouble to conceal. In all the time she had lived in Amsterdam she had never been inside one of the many diamond showrooms—though occasionally she had paused to look in at the windows, causing Duncan to accuse her of being a crypto-capitalist.

The showroom was large, with a pale marble floor, and lit by dozens of spotlights concealed in the high ceiling. The walls were lined with locked glass cases, where the most fabulous jewellery was tastefully displayed on swathes of dark blue velvet.

But it seemed as though there was an equivalent value circulating in the room, around the wrists and throats of the women present. Several of them were minor international celebrities, whom she recognised; bright and glossy in Lagerfeld and Lacroix, perfumed by Rochas and Guerlain, set to outdo each other in glamour and sophistication.

'Very grand,' she murmured drily. 'What's this all in aid of, then?'

'It is to raise money for a famine relief,' Piet supplied. 'Various benefactors have donated gifts which are to be auctioned during the evening.'

Charlie cast a sardonic eye over the laden buffet table, groaning beneath the weight of the sumptuous banquet laid out for the guests. There were enough truffles and smoked salmon and quails' eggs in aspic to sink a battleship. 'Maybe there would have had even more money for the fund if they had been a little less lavish with the catering,' she remarked caustically. 'Or won't these people give to charity unless you stuff them with caviar first?'

Piet conceded a dry laugh. 'Possibly not,' he agreed. 'However, since we are here, we might as well help to eat it. Will you try some of these quenelles?'

'Piet—how good of you to lend us your support!' An elderly woman, still extremely elegant, came forward to greet him with an affectionate kiss.

'Good evening, Maria,' he responded warmly. 'We were delighted to come. May I introduce my companion, Miss Charlotte Heller? Charlie, this is Countess Von Kudlich, who has organised this evening's events.'

His warning glance was unneccessary—natural grace, as much as her father's strict training, would have prevented her from voicing her critical opinions. And, to be fair, she conceded privately, a great deal of well meaning effort must have gone into preparing for such a sumptuous occasion.

'How do you do?' she murmured, briefly shaking the countess's gloved hand.

'Good evening, my dear. It is so nice to see you young people turning out to aid such a good cause. We have had some marvellous donations! Really, Piet, your offer of a day-trip in your helicopter was an inspired idea—I'm sure it's going to be one of the most popular lots when the bidding starts. Have you purchased your catalogue yet? Only fifty guilders.' A pale young woman, bearing a pile of glossy catalogues, materialised at her side. 'In fact, you know, the advertising alone has almost brought us up to our target,' the countess added with satisfaction. 'Isn't that marvellous?'

'It is indeed,' responded Piet blandly, reaching into his pocket to draw out his wallet.

Other guests were arriving behind them. 'Ah! I spy money-bags,' the countess confided, her eyes dancing merrily. 'I must go and fawn. Hurry, dear; give Meneer Den Ouden his catalogue, and come with me.'

Charlie watched her sweep away across the room, a little bemused. She sensed somehow that the irony of having to lay on such a glittering occasion in order to prise out donations was not lost on the countess. 'What a character,' she remarked quietly.

'Indeed,' agreed Piet wryly. 'And a most determined fund-raiser. It is quite impossible to refuse her anything. Fifty guilders for a catalogue—that is practically extortion!'

He was laughing, and Charlie felt her heart flutter; he was even more dangerously attractive when he laughed. To hide her emotions, she moved over to examine the display in one of the glass cabinets that lined the walls. A large section-diagram showed how the diamonds were found—in deep pipes within the blue kimberlite ore. And in front, on a velvet cushion, was a handful of small, grubby, crystalline pebbles.

'Are those diamonds?' she asked, surprised.

Piet nodded. 'They have not yet been cut. Each of those would probably yield about a half-carat stone— depending, of course, on the presence of any serious flaws that might have to be excluded.'

'Do they actually cut them here?'

'Of course. There is a workroom on the next floor...'

'Ah, was there ever a woman who could resist a diamond, eh, Piet?'

A gratingly patronising voice made her turn sharply. A plump little man in a dapper suit had come over to join them. Charlie had to suppress an urge to giggle—the man's head was almost completely bald, but in a vain attempt to conceal it he had carefully plastered four or five long strands of hair across the shiny dome. Piet observed her twitching lips, and slanted her a warning look.

'Won't you introduce me to the young lady, Piet?'

'Of course. Charlie, this is Meneer Van Leiden.' Something in the tone of his voice hinted to her that, although the man had used his first name, they were not particularly friends.

'Charlie? But surely that is a boy's name?' He chortled with laughter at the joke she had heard a million times since her early schooldays. 'And you are certainly not a boy.'

Charlie forced an acid smile. Meneer Van Leiden might appear to be a personage of some consequence, but he wasn't above letting his eyes linger in leering approval on the faint hint of shadow between her breasts instead of meeting her eyes as he spoke to her.

'Miss Heller was just enquiring about the cutting of the stones,' Piet intervened, his voice very level.

'Ah, yes. Well, of course, it is a very skilled job. Each stone takes many hours to cut.' He snapped his fingers peremptorily to summon a younger man who had been hovering near by, a faceless grey suit whose only function appeared to be to carry the second key that was required to open the cabinet. 'First it is necessary to examine the stone for flaws.' He took a loupe-glass from his pocket, and, handing her one of the diamonds, he invited her to study it.

Holding the stone to the light, she could see now that there were just a few very tiny flecks embedded within it to mar its perfect purity.

'Now that one would be designated VVS2, which is the third grade,' Meneer Van Leiden explained. 'And the colour is good—rare white. Quite a valuable stone.' He placed it back carefully with the others and locked the cabinet, moving on to the next one.

'Once the stone has been marked, which is the job of our most experienced grader, it is imbedded in a shell of wax, to be cut. Of course, great care must be taken to judge which planes will split. Then a saw of hardened bronze is used, rotating at a very high speed. After that it is mounted on a lathe, and ground by a second diamond to create the facets—fifty-seven to each stone. And so we come to the final result.' With a flourish he opened the cabinet, and took out a ring, which he held out to her on the palm of his hand.

Charlie gazed at it in a kind of awe. The ring was ultra-modern, almost sculptural in design; a wide band of white gold, with one solitary diamond mounted on it. It must have been worth a fortune. But it wasn't the monetary value that attracted her—it was the perfection of the stone, so pure, so strong...a symbol of love itself. The manner of its creation, in heat and pressure, deep underground, suggested to her vivid imagination that it should still be hot to the touch.

'Why don't you try it on?' suggested Piet, his voice low and quiet, as if he knew he was part of her dream.

She hesitated, her brain seemingly unable to relay any instructions to her hands. So he picked it up himself, and, lifting her left hand, he slid it on to her third finger. Slowly she lifted her eyes to met his; her heart seemed almost to have stopped beating. It fitted perfectly, as if it had been made for her.

But it was only an illusion, she reminded herself swiftly. She was only trying the ring on to admire it.

As she held up her hand the eternal fire at the heart of the stone seemed to flare into life. She swallowed hard, struggling to drag herself back to reality.

'It's . . . it's a beautiful ring,' she managed, forcing a light laugh. 'I almost wish I could keep it.'

The pompous little man chuckled. 'A beautiful ring for a beautiful woman,' he prosed, his piggy little eyes crawling all over her. 'Maybe some lucky man will buy it for you some day, eh?'

Charlie felt an uncomfortable glow of heat in her cheeks, and quickly tugged the ring off, handing it back to him. 'Oh, I doubt it,' she drawled with a dismissive shrug. 'Who'd want an engagement-ring? It's just a symbol of fascist male dominance.'

Meneer Van Leiden looked taken aback by her tart response, and Piet took her arm in a warning grip. 'Thank you, Dirk,' he said evenly. 'Please excuse us. Charlie, shall we try a little more of the buffet?'

She slanted a wary look up at him as he led her firmly but discreetly across the room. 'I'm sorry,' she murmured wryly. 'But he was such a creep!'

'Dirk van Leiden is a very wealthy and important man, and I frequently have to do business with him.'

'But you have to admit, he did look ridiculous,' she pleaded earnestly, gazing up at him. A slight twitch of his lips betrayed an amusement he couldn't quite suppress. 'Every time he moved I thought those strands of hair were going to fall down in his eyes,' she persisted, longing to persuade him to admit that she was right.

'I know,' he conceded at last, though reluctantly. 'But when you are the head of one of the most prestigious diamond houses in Europe few people are going to tell you that you should get another hairdresser.'

She gurgled with laughter. 'Thank heavens for Brylcreem,' she chuckled. 'It was all I could do to keep my face straight.'

Piet slanted her a look of sardonic humour. 'I suppose I should have known better than to bring you,' he sighed with wry resignation. 'I might have known you would say something controversial.'

'I'll behave myself from now on,' she promised earnestly, though her eyes were dancing. 'Cross my heart.'

Soon after that the auction began; people were eagerly bidding way over the odds for the privilege of occupying a private box at a performance of the Dutch National Ballet, or playing eighteen holes with a famous golfer at the Amsterdam Golf Club.

As the guests mingled around the buffet table Charlie found herself being introduced to more of Piet's business aquaintances. The talk was mostly of finance and the state of the stock-market. Charlie found it every bit as tedious as she had feared, but her father's rigorous training in the art of social chit-chat stood her in good stead, winning her a smile of approval from Piet.

The evening wore interminably on, and Charlie's feet were beginning to hurt—she had forgotten how these sandals pinched. Did she dare take them off? No one would notice—she could just slip them off very discreetly, and hide them under the long white tablecloth that covered the buffet table.

Piet glanced down at her, startled, as she slowly shrunk several inches at his elbow. 'I'm sorry—my feet were killing me,' she whispered, wriggling her toes in grateful relief.

His mouth compressed, but he didn't seem to be angry—that was definitely a glimmer of humour lurking in his eyes. 'I did warn you that it would not be the sort of occasion you would enjoy,' he reminded her quietly.

She slanted him a look of quizzical curiosity. 'Are *you* enjoying yourself?'

'Not particularly,' he conceded, a flicker of dry humour in his eyes. 'But then, I did not come to enjoy myself—it is simply the sort of function I am compelled to attend from time to time. And it is, after all, for a good cause.'

'You mean, apart from the chance to do a little business?' she enquired, a trace of sarcasm in her voice.

He conceded her point with a wry smile. 'Quite. Indeed, it is evident that the value of such an opportunity to advertise their wares has not escaped the attention of our hosts,' he added, casting a cynical eye to where Dirk van Leiden was again going through his sales-patter over a necklace that would have fed the famine victims for a month.

Charlie was silent. It was something of a surprise to her to learn that Piet had some sympathy with her views. She had expected him to be like her father—scornful, dismissive. But then, he really wasn't a bit like her father, she reminded herself. Oh, he had a well developed sense of responsibility—maybe a little *too* well developed. And he was very respectable—on the surface.

But it was only on the surface. With a little flurry of heat she remembered the way he had kissed her

just a few short hours ago, the way his hot mouth
had devoured her breast through her cotton T-shirt...
Oh, no, under that respectable façade there was an
altogether different animal...

'Ah, Miss Heller!' She started as she found Meneer
Van Leiden at her elbow again, his leering gaze fixed
once more on her faint cleavage. 'Are you enjoying
yourself?'

She edged a little away from him. 'Y... yes, thank
you,' she responded on a brittle smile, mindful of
Piet's warning.

He clucked reprovingly over her half-empty plate.
'But you're hardly eating anything,' he protested. 'I'm
sure that a pretty young thing like you must have a
very healthy appetite!'

'No, it's all right...'

'Have you tried the pâté de foie gras? I really do
recommend it.'

She shook her head, her cold stare trying to warn
him not to persist. But he was too thick-skinned to
notice. He picked up a crouton, and spread it thickly
with the greasy pink paste.

'Here,' he insisted, jabbing it towards her.

She drew back sharply, turning her head aside. 'No,
thank you,' she reiterated forcefully. 'I don't like it.'

'How do you know that until you've tried it?' he
teased as if indulging a small child.

'I can't stand the thought of the way they make it,'
she snapped, giving up all effort at restraint. 'All those
poor geese, being force-fed. It's cruel.' Her voice had
risen, and several people had turned to stare. She felt
her cheeks flush pink, but she wasn't going to back
down. 'Well, it is,' she insisted. 'I think it's wrong to

treat animals like that just so people can indulge their revolting greedy tastes.'

There was a moment of astonished silence. Close behind her she felt Piet stiffen, and fleetingly regretted that she had broken her promise yet again. But her chin was tilted up in resolute defiance—there were some things she believed in too strongly to recant.

It was the wife of a German banker that Piet had been talking to who stepped smoothly into the breach. 'So you're from England, Miss Heller?' she remarked conversationally. 'How long have you been staying in Amsterdam?'

Charlie let go her breath silently, allowing herself to be diverted. 'Oh, about six months,' she responded, feeling the tension around her ease.

'Indeed? And are you here to work, or for a holiday?'

'I'm here to paint.' She smiled a little diffidently, unsure whether her unproductive occupation would meet with much approval in this company. 'I'm an artist.'

'Really? How interesting.'

The banker had paused in his discussion with Piet to look at her as if she were some strange specimen in a zoo.

'And what do you paint?' the wife enquired, valiantly pursuing the topic.

'Oh, most things—still life, figures, landscapes. I find a lot of inspiration in Amsterdam,' she added, hoping to win a crumb of approval. 'It's a beautiful city.'

'Oh, yes, indeed,' the older woman agreed readily. 'Quite charming.'

'So you're an artist?' Meneer Van Leiden was not to be left out. He chuckled in patronising indulgence. 'And have you sold any of your paintings yet?'

Charlie felt a warning kick on her ankle from behind, but it wasn't necessary—she would have responded with that bland, 'No,' anyway.

'Well, even Van Gogh didn't manage to sell any paintings during his lifetime,' he reminded her in a condescendingly comforting tone. 'And now see how much his paintings are worth. More than eighty million dollars for a self-portrait! Of course, it's a shame it had to go to Japan,' he added, as if that was comparable to its disappearing down a black hole in space. 'But then, I suppose that's where the money is these days.'

'Well, quite frankly,' remarked the banker's wife, 'I'd a good deal rather have it go abroad than it be the subject of the kind of unpleasant bargaining that took place over his *Irises*. Really, it was most unseemly.'

The banker seemed to think it was incumbent on him to join in the conversation. 'Ah, yes—I understand it was purchased by the Getty Museum,' he commented ponderously. 'And the market was protected, which is the main thing.'

'Oh, of course,' agreed Meneer Van Leiden earnestly. 'But it demonstrates, I think, how very careful one must be when choosing art. A disaster like that can easily rock the market.'

Charlie was listening to this discourse with growing loathing. Even Piet, to give him credit, looked faintly uncomfortable about it, his smile a little fixed.

The banker nodded solemnly. 'I think the galleries have a great deal of responsibility if they are going to become involved in the business of financing such transactions,' he prosed.

'Of course, it's with the modern painters that the real investment value lies,' Meneer Van Leiden went on, complacently displaying his knowledge of the subject. 'If you know the right ones to pick. The book value of Jasper Johns has gone up enormously since that American publisher paid . . . what was it, nearly eighteen million? Of course, that was a very shrewd move on his part—he already owns one of the best Johns collections, so it's done him a very great deal of good.'

Charlie could contain herself no longer. 'Is that the only thing that matters to you about a painting?' she burst out. 'Its investment value? I bet you couldn't tell a Sisley from a Cézanne.' People were turning to stare, but she was past caring. 'I bet if I was to paint something right here on the tablecloth you wouldn't know whether to hang it in the Stedelijk Museum or chuck it in the washing-up!'

That crazy demon had gripped her again. All these stuffy people, with their public virtue and their private greed—they were just like her father! She'd like to take them all by their scrawny necks and dump them in the canal! Well, at least she could do the next best thing.

Barefoot, she skipped up on to the table and began quickly moving things aside to make a space in the centre of the tablecloth, pristine white and challenging, like a canvas. The food and sauces made excellent paints, and, lacking brushes, she used her fingers.

It was so satisfying to make great, sweeping swirls of colour, red and orange and brown, as free and wild and angry as she felt in her heart. 'There!' She glared down at the shocked gathering, especially that ugly little man with his silly bald head. 'Now stuff that in your bank account and watch it grow!'

Piet hadn't moved; he stood watching her in a kind of stunned horror, but as she finished her act of rebellion with a wide gesture of her arms she could sense his anger, smouldering up inside him like a fire-storm that was about to explode. And suddenly the rage that had buoyed her up seemed to slip away, and her bold attack on the bounds of convention seemed merely stupid and childish.

It was with only a sulky defiance that she regarded her artistic effort, and decided it needed something else. A few dribbles of taramasalata—after all, she had ruined the tablecloth anyway, along with any hope that Piet might ever forgive her.

Abruptly he stepped forward, and, grasping her wrist in steel fingers, he dragged her down from the table. 'I must extend my sincerest apologies for this,' he grated, bowing slightly to the stunned countess. 'I will, of course, pay for the damage, and make a donation to your committee to recompense for the embarrassment and inconvenience to your guests. Now if you will please excuse us...'

He dragged Charlie out into the street, not even pausing to allow her to put her shoes back on. He strode on down the road, unaware or uncaring that she was having to run to keep up with him. But she didn't protest—in his present mood she didn't dare.

'What did you think you were doing?' he demanded furiously. 'Are you drunk? Are you crazy? I think perhaps I should telephone your father at once, and have him come and put you in an asylum. Never, never have I seen such behaviour.'

'I'm sorry.' She was breathless and sobbing, struggling to keep up with him. 'Oh, Piet, I'm so sorry. I don't know what got into me. It was just that he made me so cross, talking about paintings like that, and the way he kept leering at me all the time. Suddenly I just saw red.'

'You may think yourself lucky that I am not a violent man, or I would certainly have put you over my knee—for that is what you richly deserve. Or is that what you want?' he demanded, stopping and turning so suddenly that she stumbled against him. 'You have constantly sought to provoke me, from the first moment we met. Is that what turns you on? To be beaten?'

'No!' She stared up at him in horror. 'I didn't do it to provoke you, honestly, Piet. I didn't mean to make you angry.' Her hand was against the hard wall of his chest, sensing the fierce masculine power in him, and suddenly she felt very tiny and vulnerable. 'I'm sorry, Piet,' she whispered, all her heart in her eyes. 'I'm really sorry.'

Angrily he drew her closer against him, crushing her roughly in his arms. 'Do you think that is all you have to do?' he rasped, still angry but now unmistakably aroused as well. 'Say you are sorry, and gaze up at me with those appealing eyes? And I will forgive you, and forget what a fool you have made of me?'

The wild sway of her emotions was making her heart pound so fast that it was difficult to breathe. She had been angry, and then distressed, and then frightened, and now . . . now she only knew how very much she wanted him to kiss her. Her lips parted on a sweet sigh of anticipation, and her lashes fluttered down to veil her eyes as his head bent towards hers ...

But then abruptly he pushed her away. 'No. I'm sorry, but you cannot so easily wind me around your little finger, as you have no doubt wound so many men before, with the promise of your delectable body. As I have said, I do not find such shop-soiled goods attractive.'

She hadn't realised that they had reached his building until he dragged his keys from his pocket and opened the front door. He thrust her inside, almost making her stumble, but he didn't follow her. Instead he turned away, stalking off down the street, his hands thrust deep into his pockets.

'Where are you going?' she pleaded, bewildered and bereft.

'For a walk,' he barked, not turning back.

'But ... what should I do?'

'Just stay out of my sight,' he growled. 'Otherwise I'm not sure what I might do to you.'

CHAPTER SIX

THE floorboards beneath the thin sleeping-bag were hard. Charlie grunted as she turned over, trying to find a comfortable position to lie in. She didn't like to think too hard about what might be lurking in the dark corners of the lofty warehouse—mice, and spiders, and worse... With a shudder she closed her eyes tightly and tried to sleep, ignoring the bunch of kids gathered around the single bar of an electric fire in the middle of the room, strumming guitars and singing protest songs.

'Charlie—hey, why don't you come on over and join us?'

Stuart—that friend of Duncan's who had always been hanging around the houseboat, and who had brought the drugs on board—had crawled over to her corner. She kept her eyes firmly closed, pretending to be asleep, but he shook her shoulder.

'Hey, Charlie, come on. We're having a good time. Why are you all on your own here in the corner?'

'Go away, Stuart,' she grated, refusing to open her eyes. 'I'm trying to sleep.'

'What for? It's early yet.' He laughed unpleasantly, and began to unzip her sleeping-bag. 'On the other hand, maybe I'll come and join you instead. Shove over and let me in.'

'Go away!' Angrily she banged his hand away from the zip. 'Just leave me alone, OK? I don't want to

talk to you, and I *certainly* don't want to share a
sleeping-bag with you.'

'Oh, now, Charlie,' he coaxed sneeringly, leaning
over her. 'That isn't very friendly——'

'I believe I heard the young lady ask you to go
away.'

Charlie gasped in shock as a tall, dark figure loomed
above them. 'Piet! What...?'

'What am I doing here?' he enquired drily. 'I came
to fetch you.'

'But....' Stuart had melted away out of sight, and
it was Piet who knelt beside her sleeping-bag now. He
wasn't wearing a suit tonight—he was wearing a pair
of hip-hugging blue jeans, and a zip-up tracksuit
jacket over a black T-shirt. The image was casual—
but the glint in his eyes was a warning. 'How did you
find me?' she asked weakly.

'I asked around among some old friends. I knew
the places to look—I was young myself once.' He
added the last with a wry smile, although the way he
looked tonight made Charlie realise that it wasn't
really so very long ago.

She had only half expected that he would come after
her. After that awful scene last night she wouldn't
have been surprised if he had wiped his hands of her
completely. As soon as she had let herself back into
the flat she had packed a bag and fled, scuttling away
to hide in the back-streets of Amsterdam, among her
own kind, where she hoped he wouldn't find her.

She sat up in the sleeping-bag, wrapping her arms
defensively around her knees, conscious that she
looked a grubby mess—there was nowhere here in this
semi-derelict building that she could get a proper

wash. 'I'm not coming back,' she declared defiantly. 'You can't make me.'

'Please stop behaving like a spoilt child,' he returned, his voice strained with patience. 'May I remind you—again—that it is a condition of your bail that you reside at my address? You are at present in breach of that condition.'

'So?' In her humiliation at his contempt, she retreated further behind that barrier of brash rebellion she had so perfected. 'You don't have to worry—I'm not planning to skip the country or anything. You won't lose your money.'

'I am not concerned about the money. It is only a small amount to me, and I am quite sure your father would insist on recompensing me anyway.'

'What would you know about my father?' she challenged with a toss of her head.

'I have spoken to him on the telephone. Naturally he was concerned to hear of your arrest, and your subsequent disappearance . . .'

'Oh, I'm sure he was,' she countered, bitter tears stinging her eyes. 'I'm sure you had a jolly nice chat about how wayward I am. And I suppose he's going to drop everything and come hotfooting up here to Amsterdam to sort everything out?'

'Regrettably not.'

'No—of course he wouldn't. He's *far* too busy.' The façade was crumbling rapidly. 'Just go away and leave me alone,' she pleaded, bitter tears stinging the backs of her eyes. 'I'm sorry I've been such a nuisance to you. Well, now you're well rid of me. Don't worry—I'll show up in court when I have to.'

'That is reassuring, but it is a little beside the point,' he returned evenly. 'You may have forgotten that we both made promises to the Commissar d'Instruction. You may not attach a great deal of significance to the giving of your word, but I do—it is my honour and my reputation. Does that mean nothing to you?'

She peered up at him from beneath her lashes, an uncomfortable stab of guilt twisting in her heart. He had got her released from custody, and she hadn't exactly repaid him very well. 'I'm sorry,' she murmured, shamefaced. 'I didn't mean to put you in an awkward position.'

'You haven't, as yet.' His tone was a little more gentle. 'If you return with me now, and abide by the conditions of your bail from now on, no more needs to be said.'

He held out his hand. For a long moment she hesitated, unable to look up and meet his eyes. There was rather more to it, on her part at least, than simply meeting the conditions of her bail. She should have known from the beginning that she couldn't live in his apartment without taking a serious risk with her heart.

And now she had fallen in love with him. It didn't seem possible—she, the rebel, the wild one, falling for a respectable businessman in a suit. Goodness, her father would be delighted! But that didn't seem to matter—nothing that used to matter seemed important any more.

And if she went back with him now it was going to be even more difficult. Because there was no danger that he was going to fall in love with her. Oh, he wanted her, certainly—though not so much that he couldn't hold it in check when it suited him. But he didn't have a very high opinion of her—and she could hardly blame him for that, since she had deliberately set out to make him think the worst of her.

And if he knew the truth? Somehow she didn't think that he was the type to be interested in a totally inexperienced young girl, either. His sort of woman would be mature, sophisticated, elegant—like that redhaired French girl who had come up to the apartment yesterday...

'Charlie?'

He was waiting for her to respond, and she knew that she really had no choice. It wasn't just a matter of breaching her bail conditions; she would always do whatever Piet wanted her to do. Reluctantly she placed her hand in his, and let him help her to her feet.

She had only brought a few things with her, and in truth she would be glad to leave this horrible, dirty place behind. Maybe she was beginning to grow away from her old crowd of friends, she reflected thoughtfully. They seemed to find little wrong with the thought of staying here.

She picked up her bag and swung it across her shoulder, letting Piet take her arm and lead her to the door. One of the long-standing members of the commune, a street musician who was much respected by the kids, glanced up as they passed.

'OK, Piet? I see you found her.'

'Yes—thanks for your help, Wim. I'll see you around.'

'Sure, man. Mind how you go.' He lifted one hand in a casual wave of farewell, and turned back to his guitar-playing, a hand-rolled cigarette dangling loosely from the side of his mouth.

'How did you know Wim Simonsz?' Charlie enquired curiously as they walked down the dark stairs.

'He's an old friend.'

She slanted him a questioning look. '*Wim's* an old friend of yours?'

'I told you, I was young myself once,' he conceded, an echo of reluctance in his voice. 'We had a houseboat, not unlike yours, me and Wim and a bunch of others. They were good times.'

'Was that when you used to race stock-cars?' she asked, grasping at this opportunity to learn a little more about him.

'I was racing then, yes,' he agreed.

'Before you took over the family business?'

'Yes.'

They had reached the street, and his car was waiting. Charlie slipped into the passenger-seat, still thoughtful. He didn't seem to like talking about his youth. Why not? He had said they were good times— but they had ended abruptly when his brother died and he had taken over the business, taken over the responsibility. Did he regret their passing? But his manner warned her not to ask any more now—maybe she would get an opportunity another time.

It didn't take long to drive through Amsterdam's busy streets to the Herengracht. It was strange, but as the car drew in to the side of the canal, and they walked across the narrow cobbled street to the front door, she felt as if she was coming home.

Home. She had never had a home, not a proper one—a succession of boarding-schools, a succession of scruffy digs didn't count as home. And home certainly wasn't with her father, in any of the three soulless apartments he maintained in Brussels, Luxembourg and Strasbourg, moving between them as the European parliament moved around from one of its locations to the next.

'Are you hungry?' enquired Piet as they rode up in the private lift to the top floor.

'Yes, I am,' she admitted, realising that she hadn't eaten all day—she had had no appetite for food. 'But I could do with a bath first.'

He nodded. 'You have your bath, and I'll cook us something.'

She risked a squint up at him. 'You really can cook, then?' she asked.

'Well enough,' he confirmed with a smile. 'A bachelor needs to be able to take care of himself.'

Oh, yes—a bachelor. That was a timely reminder, she reflected as she followed him into the apartment. Why had he never married? There must have been scores of girls. But clearly he liked his life the way it was. Her own stay, to him, was a strictly temporary arrangement.

'I'll . . . go and have my bath, then,' she murmured, and slipped away to her own comfortable room.

It was so pleasant to be able to strip off all her clothes and sink into the warm, soft water. She had swirled in a generous ladle of bath oil, and the bubbles rose around her luxuriantly, making her feel like a film star. She scooped some up in her hands, blowing on them and laughing as they drifted like snow.

A tap on the door brought her head round in alarm. 'May I come in?' asked Piet's voice.

'Oh . . .' She swallowed hard, and sank down in the water so that the bubbles modestly covered her breasts. 'Yes.'

The door opened, and Piet appeared, a steaming mug in his hand. 'I've brought you some hot chocolate,' he said. 'It felt cold in that place, even though it was warm outside.'

'Yes,' she agreed, her voice a little unsteady. 'It was quite damp.' Cautiously she reached out one arm from the bubbles, and took the mug from him. 'Thank you.'

'You shouldn't have gone there,' he said, sitting down on the edge of the bath. 'You might not have been safe.'

She managed a light laugh, her heart beating far too fast at having him so near. 'Oh, it was all right,' she assured him. 'I can take care of myself—I've been doing it for years.'

'Can you?' His voice was serious. 'What about that chap who was trying to climb into your sleeping-bag?'

'Stu? Oh, he's harmless—I can cope with him.'

'Isn't he the one who brought the drugs on to your boat?'

'Yes.' Under the water she was twirling her fingers, watching the patterns it made in the bubbles. 'But I didn't know about that, honestly, Piet.' She lifted her eyes to his, and found herself almost hypnotised as he seemed to search right into her soul.

'Was he one of the ones who lived on the boat?' he asked quietly.

'No. Well, he stayed sometimes.' She could feel a blush rising to her cheeks—but maybe he would think it was just the warmth of the water.

'And did you ever sleep with him?'

'No.'

For a long moment that mesmerising gaze held hers, as if he was judging whether she was telling the truth. And then he smiled. 'Good.' He scooped up a little of the bubbles on one finger, and deposited it on the dainty tip of her nose. 'Enjoy your bath,' he said, rising to his feet. 'Dinner will be ready when you are.'

As he closed the door behind him she sank down further into the water, closing her eyes. Why had he been so concerned whether or not she had slept with Stu? Was he *jealous*? A glorious warmth was spreading through her body, and she streched her arms languorously above her head, smiling to herself. Maybe Mr Iceberg was beginning to melt after all.

But it wasn't exactly a romantic dinner for two that Piet had prepared. There were no candles on the table—the room was brightly, if subtly lit—and it wasn't a romantic Debussy piano concerto drifting from the hi-fi system, but Pink Floyd's *Dark Side of the Moon*.

He must have noticed the wry twist of her smile, because he lifted one straight eyebrow in enquiry. 'This is all right?' he asked, nodding towards the hi-fi.

'Oh . . . yes, fine,' she agreed quickly, setting aside her disappointment. Maybe she was hoping for too much too soon.

'Sit down,' he invited with a casual wave of his hand. 'I will bring in the food from the kitchen.'

He had laid two places on opposite sides of the dining table, and Charlie sat herself down on one of the chairs, her appetite stirring as she scented the wafting aroma of Indonesian spices. Piet brought in a large bowl of *nasi goreng*, delicious fried rice, and then a tray bearing a selection of dishes—beef satay, hot pimentos, and of course the fierce peppery peanut sauce.

'Mmm—it smells delicious,' she approved, surveying the spread. 'I'm starving!'

'Good.' His grey eyes were smiling. 'Help yourself.'

Her father had often criticised her for putting too much food on her plate, but she never had the least trouble eating it. By rights she should have been as round as a balloon—maybe it was her quicksilver energy that burned it all off so rapidly, leaving her with her dainty, slender figure.

Piet, at least, seemed not to mind at all if she was a little greedy, smiling indulgently as she piled up a mound of rice and decorated it with spoonfuls from each of the dishes. Her small white teeth nibbled a piece of beef satay off its wooden skewer, and she sighed in delight.

'Lovely—you really *are* a good cook,' she declared. 'Do you have any other hidden talents?'

'A few, perhaps,' he conceded with a trace of dry humour. 'Not as many as you, however. I have looked at some of your paintings. They are very, very good.'

'Thank you.' His praise warmed her—but she couldn't help wondering what he had thought of that one of Sara. She didn't quite have the nerve to ask him.

'You promised that you would accept a commission to paint a mural in my offices downstairs,' he reminded her. 'When could you begin?'

She looked at him in surprise. 'Were you really serious about that?' she queried. 'I thought...'

'By all means I was serious,' he insisted. 'The wall is about four or five metres long, and gets little natural light. What sort of thing do you think you might paint?'

'Well...what do you want?'

'Maybe...' He paused to think. 'A scene of Amsterdam would be nice. But not as it is now— something more... medieval, I think.'

'Yes!' she agreed, her eyes sparkling. 'Amsterdam in the fifteenth century. A street with houses, and the canal, and people going about their business. I could go to the museums to get ideas.'

'Certainly. There is a fine exhibition in the Historisch Museum, behind the Begijnenhofje. That should give you much of the information you need. Of course, before 1452 the houses were mostly of wood; then there was a great fire, and it became law to build only in stone.'

'When were these houses built?' she asked him.

'On the Herengracht? Oh, about 1600. That was the time of the Golden Age, when Dutch shipping was going all around the world, and many rich merchants lived here. Naturally, each wanted the finest house, the most elaborate gable—you will see some splendid ones along here. But sadly most of the houses are now too big for private residences—most have been converted into offices.'

'At least they haven't been knocked down to make way for a ghastly modern city centre, like in most places,' she reminded him.

'Heaven forbid! Fortunately now most of the buildings are protected by law. And there can be no excuses for not carrying out a proper renovation,' he added with a quirk of dry humour. 'There is even an official yard where one can purchase original-style windows and doors!'

'Really?' Charlie gurgled with laughter. 'Typical Dutch efficiency! But what really worries me,' she went on seriously, 'is what will happen if all these horror stories about global warming are true. If the sea level rises, what will happen to Amsterdam?'

He smiled wryly. 'Indeed—that could be a very serious problem. And not only for Amsterdam. There are many parts of the world that would suffer badly.'

She nodded. 'I was reading only the other day that some of the islands in the Pacific could just disappear altogether!'

'It is to be hoped that it is not beyond the wit of mankind to find a solution before it is too late,' he concluded. 'Have you had enough to eat, or would you like a little more?'

'Oh, no—that was plenty, thank you. And it was really good. You're a much better cook than I am— I can't even boil an egg. I wouldn't make a very good wife, I'm afraid!'

Piet laughed with sardonic humour. 'Indeed—that is a role that really would not suit you at all,' he agreed readily.

Charlie felt as if a knife had punctured her heart. She had spoken in all innocence, drifting along on her own dreams. But without even knowing it he had shattered those dreams. Fortunately he had risen to his feet, and picked up the empty rice bowl to carry it into the kitchen, so he didn't notice the tears she had to blink back from her eyes.

Instinctively she retreated within her brittle defences, putting on that 'don't care' act again. 'Marriage is all a con anyway,' she declared with cynical disdain. 'It's just a form of legalised prostitution.'

He slanted her a look of quizzical amusement as he came back for the other dishes. 'And you don't intend to have anything to do with it?'

'No way!' She unfolded herself lithely from her seat. 'Want a hand with the washing-up?'

'Fortunately we may safely leave that menial task to the dishwasher,' he informed her, that smile of enigmatic humour still lurking in his eyes.

'Oh...good.' Was he laughing at her? Or, worse still, was he mocking her? He was remarkably astute at guessing close to the truth. To give herself a little time to steady her shaken nerves she strolled over to the window to examine the pot-plants she had established on the sill.

'You're looking very fine,' she murmured to one of her favourites, a rose-flowered begonia of a soft amber hue. 'Do you like it here? Are you getting enough sunshine?'

'Do you always talk to your plants?'

She started away as she realised he had come up close behind her. 'Of...course,' she managed, her voice unsteady. 'It helps them to grow.'

'Really?' Now there was no mistaking the glint of amusement in his eye. He was teasing her.

'As a matter of fact, there have been scientific tests on it,' she informed him with dignity. 'They've even found in Africa that the trees talk to each other. There's a species of acacia that can warn each other of danger by sending a chemical signal through the air, and then they produce extra tannin to stop the antelopes eating them all.'

'Well, I never!' He was laughing openly now. 'It just goes to show what a very strange place the world is.'

Charlie gazed up at him, feeling herself drawn again by that strange, mesmerising power in his eyes. But this time she was fighting it, refusing to let him overpower her will. 'You learn something new every day,' she remarked carelessly, turning her shoulder on him and giving her attention to her plants again.

'It seems at least that you are doing something that is good for them,' Piet commented, an edge of tension in his voice that would have been imperceptible had she not been so finely attuned to listen for it. 'They are certainly flourishing.'

'Another of my many talents,' she returned airily. 'They give this place a bit of life, anyway,' she added, casting a faintly disparaging glance around the elegant room, as if she didn't think much of it.

'They certainly do.' He had come up close behind her again. 'And so do you.' His voice was low and husky, beguiling. As if in a dream himself, he put out his hand to her hair. 'Your hair is like candy-floss,' he murmured, twirling one curling strand idly through his fingers.

A shimmer of heat ran through her at his touch, but she was determined not to let him see her weakness. There was just one sure way to put him off. Very deliberately she turned, leaning back against the window-sill, her body provocatively aligned to emphasise every curve. 'Do you want to go to bed with me?' she challenged brazenly.

For an instant he looked taken aback, but then he laughed in bitter self-mockery. 'Yes, I do,' he grated out harshly. 'Does that give you satisfaction? Does it compensate your bruised ego for the fact that your father has no time to show you love to know that you can make most other men fall at your feet?'

'Don't psychoanalyse me!' she warned furiously, alarmed by the accuracy of his perception. 'I'm *me*. I don't need my father, and I don't need you.'

'Maybe not. But what you do need is a lesson.'
Those grey eyes flamed with an angry light. 'Damn
you, you could almost drive a man to insanity!'

Alarmed, she tried to side-step out of his way, but
he caught her roughly by the shoulders and slammed
her back against the wall. Staring up at him, she
realised with a stab of horror that she had goaded
him too far. She tried to scream, but it was too late;
his mouth descended on hers in a kiss that was a
ruthless assault, crushing her lips apart, his tongue
plundering into the deepest corners of her mouth in
a savage invasion.

She tried to struggle free, but she didn't stand a
chance. His fingers had laced into her hair, cruelly
dragging back her head. Her slender body was crushed
against his, making her devastatingly aware of the
fierce male arousal that was mingled with his anger.

This wasn't what was supposed to have happened.
He should have turned away from her in disgust—
but he never reacted the way she expected him to. He
didn't seem to care that he was hurting her—dear God,
was he going to drag her into the bedroom and force
her to deliver on what he had clearly taken as an
invitation?

She felt him rip apart the buttons on her blouse, a
gesture that she knew was meant to be an insult. She
had a bra on for once, but it was the merest scrap of
lace and no defence against him—with a fierce jerk
he had snapped it off, and his hands were on her naked
breasts, punishing her with his humiliating caresses.

But she couldn't control her response; it was like a
fever in her blood. She felt her aching breasts swell
into his palm, her tender nipples hardening in a
shaming betrayal of her arousal. Her bones were

melting in the torrid heat, and she had to cling to him to stop herself from falling, every inch of her yearning to submit to his fierce demand.

He let her go so abruptly that she fell to her knees. 'Bitch,' he muttered fiercely. 'That's what you want, isn't it? To drag me down to your level? You cheapen everything you touch.' He dragged in a harsh breath, visibly struggling to regain his self-control. 'There is no need for you to run away again,' he grated through clenched teeth. 'I vowed I wouldn't take advantage of the situation you find yourself in, and I won't—you may rest assured that there will be no repetition of this scene.' He wiped the back of his hand across his mouth, as if to wipe away all trace of her. 'I'm going out.'

She winced as he slammed the door—the sound seemed to reverberate through the whole building. Trembling, she dragged herself into a sitting position, leaning back against the wall, and tried vainly to re-fasten her blouse. Half the buttons were missing, scattered across the floor, and on hands and knees she crawled around to pick them up.

CHAPTER SEVEN

CHARLIE was almost reluctant to come out of her bedroom the next morning, a little afraid of what she would have to face. But when she finally risked it she found Piet drinking coffee in the kitchen. He greeted her with a wry smile.

'Good morning.'

'*Goedemorgen,*' she responded warily.

'I have several business meetings today—it might be quite late before I return. Please make yourself entirely at home here. And if you wish to begin on the mural Lenneke will provide any assistance necessary.'

'Thank you.' He hadn't exactly apologised for last night in so many words, but his manner seemed to be indicating a plea for a truce. She allowed him a half-smile. 'Are you really sure you want me to do one?' she asked.

'Of course.' He looked surprised. 'Why do you ask?'

'Oh...' She lifted one slim shoulder in a small shrug. 'It's just... I didn't think my work would be quite your style,' she explained diffidently. 'I tend to use a lot of primary colours, and splash the paint around a lot.'

'That sounds just right,' he said, his grey eyes glinting with a humour she didn't quite understand. 'Maybe I'll have you paint every wall in the office. I'm getting tired of beige.'

'Right.' She laughed a little uncertainly. 'Well, I'll start my research today, then, and try to have some sketches for you in a few days.'

'Excellent.' He finished his coffee, and glanced at his watch. 'Now I must go. I will see you this evening.'

She nodded. 'Goodbye, then.'

'Goodbye.'

It didn't take Charlie long to absorb herself in the fascinating medieval history of Amsterdam. A visit to the excellent museum, right in the heart of the old city, set the scene for her, and then she spent the rest of the day wandering along the oldest canals and narrow side-streets, taking Polaroid photographs, almost able to forget the tourists surging around her and the rather garish atmosphere of a district quite openly given over to the oldest profession in the world.

Leaning on the iron railing of a bridge over one of the Oudezijds, munching on a sweet *flensje* she had bought from a street stall, she could let her vivid imagination take her right back in time, and almost see what it must have been like here when the Europe all around was dark with the smoke of religious wars, and ships returning from long, long voyages to Java and the Moluccas, laden with silks and spices, could have been returning from another planet.

She was so lost in this other world she was creating that she didn't even notice the tubby little man watching her, until he approached. 'Hello—it's Miss Heller, isn't it? Charlie?'

'Oh...yes,' she responded, startling away from him.

He smiled reassuringly. 'Dirk van Leiden,' he reminded her, offering his hand. 'I had the pleasure of making your acquaintance at the reception we held for the Countess Von Kudlich's charity committee on Saturday.'

'Of... of course.' His manners were immpeccable, but there was still something about him that she didn't quite like. She shook the proffered hand politely, remembering with a twinge of embarrassment the way she had behaved at that reception. 'How do you do?'

'Are you going back to the Heren?' he enquired solicitously. 'I'll walk along with you if you like.'

'Oh... yes,' she murmured with a shade of reluctance. She had been ready to return home, but she would have preferred not to walk along with this man. But it would be rude to refuse him, so she fell into step beside him, making sure she kept a distance between them.

To her relief, he didn't attempt to come any closer. He made pleasant small talk all the way, and by the time they got back to the Den Ouden offices she was almost ready to think that she had maybe misjudged him. Almost.

Piet didn't come upstairs until after nine o'clock, and even then he brought some work with him— Charlie couldn't help wondering if that was his usual routine, or just because she was there. He accepted a cup of coffee, but mostly she stayed quiet and out of his way, working at her sketch-pad.

Over the next few days she continued with her research, visiting art galleries and libraries, getting ideas of the sort of clothes people wore, the sort of things they did. And she took her sketch-pad with her on her strolls, trying with her swift pencil to capture images and impressions—the way the jagged line of the gablestones along the roofs reflected in the shimmering water, the way the tall trees stretched out their branches across the canal. A small brown and white dog caught her eye, snuffling around by some steps, and she decided to include him as well.

There would have to be a lot of blues and browns in the mural, of course, with the canal and the buildings, but she could add colour with the clothes of the people and the goods being unloaded from the barges into the upper floors of the tall narrow buildings, on ropes slung from hoisting beams high on the gable-fronts above.

Piet continued to work late every evening. The atmosphere between them was still perhaps a little awkward, especially if by accident they should come a little too close to each other, but gradually Charlie was beginning to allow herself to relax.

He liked her sketches. Lenneke had shown her the wall that was to be painted—the main wall in the reception area of the offices downstairs. If Lenneke or indeed any of the staff were surprised by this novel intrusion into the calmly efficient atmosphere of the place they didn't show it. Seating was quickly moved forward to leave her a space to work, sheets were hung across from floor to ceiling to shield the rest of the room, and planks and step-ladders were brought in, as well as the tubs of emulsion paint she had ordered.

The first job was to paint the whole wall white. That done, she pencilled in the basic outline of the design, squaring up from her sketches or drawing freehand, leaving the details to be added as she went along. She had chosen a view as if looking down a canal from one of the bridges, leading the eye right into the centre of the picture. And she had created lots of little visual jokes—the pompous merchant in his fine robes, strolling down to visit his warehouse, about to trip over the little dog; the fat woman leaning against her hand-cart, gossiping with a friend, ignoring the toddler tugging at her skirts, who was trying to tell her that her weight had tipped the cart and her oranges were rolling into the canal.

'Ah—so this is the famous mural!'

It was the tubby man again—Dirk van Leiden. Charlie forced a smile, though she found it very hard to be friendly with him—there was just something about him that gave her the creeps. Maybe it was his eyes. 'Yes,' she managed. 'I'm sorry. I...don't usually like anyone watching me while I'm working. It puts me off.'

He chuckled. 'Ah, we all have to wait until it is finished, do we?' he queried indulgently. 'Well, don't mind me.' He backed away, his hands raised in genial apology. 'I won't peep.'

Charlie drew a steadying breath. 'Thank you,' she responded evenly, glad to see him go. Since he was a friend of Piet's, and—she had discovered—did quite a lot of business with him, supplying the industrial diamonds used in his machine tools, she didn't like to be impolite to him. But she didn't like him.

She could only work on the mural for a few hours at a time—it was necessary to wait in between for the paint to dry. And, besides, she didn't like spending all her time doing just one thing—it made her feel dull. She spent a couple of hours every day sitting with her friends in the Vondelpark, or drinking coffee in the traditional Dutch 'brown bars' around the city. And, since Piet had invited her to make herself at home, and had assured her that he had no objection to her bringing her friends up to the apartment, she had felt no qualms about asking Sara to come up and

model for her—the cool north light in the sitting-room
was perfect for drawing.

'So I said to him, "What's sauce for the goose is
sauce for the gander." Do you know, he spent the
entire evening with that Karin—you know, the one
that works in the café? He completely ignored me.'

Charlie smiled wryly. She did have some sympathy
for her friend's tangled love-life, but sometimes she
couldn't help feeling that a lot of it was acted out just
for the sake of melodrama. 'He told me the other day
that he really loves you,' she remarked soothingly. 'I
think he's just scared of getting too tied down. Are
you sure you're warm enough with nothing on, Sara?
I can turn the heating on if you like.'

'Oh, no, I'm quite OK. This is a lot better than
some of the draughty places I've had to work in.' Sara,
leaning in a negligent pose against the back of one of
Piet's stylish leather armchairs, gazed around in awe.
'This is a fabulous apartment,' she breathed. 'He must
be *loaded*.'

'Keep still,' Charlie reminded her, trying to evade
the subject. 'You keep moving your head.'

'Sorry. But come on, tell me,' Sara went on insist-
ently. 'What's he like? Is he good-looking?'

'Oh…not bad.' Charlie couldn't quite suppress the
small smile that curved her soft mouth, concentrating
all her attention on defining the smooth line of her
friend's bare shoulder.

Sara chuckled knowingly. 'Ah, come on,' she
teased. 'Karin told me all about him.'

'What are you asking me for, then?' Charlie retaliated, shifting her cross-legged position on the opposite armchair so that her sketch-pad almost hid her
blushing face.

'So he *is* good-looking,' concluded Sara in triumph. 'And is he nice?'

'Nice? Well, yes.' It was no good—the temptation to talk about her favourite subject was just too much for her. 'Sometimes he can be a bit frosty, like when I put my foot in it in front of all his friends. But if there's anything wrong he's really kind.' She tipped her head dreamily on one side. 'When I got drunk, and I was sick, he took care of me, and didn't get annoyed or anything.'

'Now that's a man worth holding on to!' declared Sara. 'What's he like in bed?' she added wickedly.

Charlie's cheeks flamed an even deeper pink. 'I don't know,' she confessed shakily. 'I haven't...'

'You haven't been to bed with him?' Sara sounded both surprised and sympathetic. 'Why not?'

'I...wanted to wait. Until I was really sure...how he felt about me.'

'But he must like you,' Sara argued. 'I mean, he had no reason to offer to stand bail for you in the first place.'

'I know. And I think he *does* like me. It's just——'

They both glanced up, startled, as the door opened. Charlie uttered a squawk of horror as she recognised Dirk van Leiden. His face registered sheer lecherous delight as he saw Sara standing there, in all her naked glory, and she returned him a look of cold indignation.

He half choked. 'Well, I... Good afternoon...I wasn't expecting...'

Piet, just behind him, had taken in the scene with his cool grey eyes. 'Please excuse us,' he said, gravely polite. 'I didn't realise you were working, Charlie. We will go back downstairs.'

'Oh, don't mind me.' Sara had reached for her clothes. 'I'll get dressed.'

'I've...finished anyway,' Charlie managed to choke out.

'Thank you.' If it weren't that Charlie was coming to know him so well she might have thought that Piet was angry. But she recognised that slight twitch at the corner of his mouth. He was trying not to smile. 'Dirk, we may look at the specifications here at my desk.' He ushered the little man over to the part of the room where he worked, flickering Charlie a look as he passed that confirmed her suspicion. He wasn't annoyed—he was amused.

The diamond merchant couldn't prevent his piggy eyes following Sara as she crossed the room. His head swivelled right round—and he bumped into a low coffee-table. Charlie swiftly covered the giggle that had sprung to her lips. 'Shall I...make you some coffee?' she offered. 'Or would you like me to leave you alone?'

'Coffee would be fine, thank you,' responded Piet, his voice not quite controlled enough to suppress the hint of mirth in it. 'Dirk?'

'Oh...yes.' He cleared his throat. 'Yes, how very kind of you. Thank you.' His eyes were still lingering on the spot where he had last seen Sara, as if he thought she had been some heavenly vision that might at any moment reappear.

Charlie retired discreetly to the kitchen and put the kettle on. A few moments later Sara, now fully dressed, joined her there. 'I'll be going,' she whispered. 'I'll see you tomorrow.'

'Goodbye, Sara,' she responded quietly. 'And I'm sorry about that.'

Sara's chuckle was wicked. 'Oh, don't worry about it,' she assured her. 'If he's so short of amusement that he has to ogle me I feel sorry for him. By the way,' she added, her eyes dancing with mischief, 'your man is *gorgeous*. And if he's not crazy about you I'm an alien from outer space.'

Charlie blushed, but Sara had already slipped away. She finished making the coffee, and took the cups over to the two men at the desk. If Sara had been right about Piet's being crazy about her he showed little sign of it, simply accepting the coffee with a brief word of thanks. Charlie moved away to the other side of the room, and picked up her sketch-pad.

Piet would be a perfect subject to draw. He was sitting close to the window, the light casting the strong bones of his face into crisp relief. Turning to a clean page, she began to sketch, capturing with a few deft strokes something of the essential masculinity of those features.

Glancing up, he noticed what she was doing and smiled faintly, making her blush. Quickly she turned over the page. A short while later he finished his discussion with Meneer Van Leiden, and showed him out of the apartment. Then he came over to lean across the back of her armchair.

She was working on the sketch of Sara, filling in some of the shadows with pencil hatching. He studied it with academic interest. 'Very good,' he approved.

'It's for the mural,' she explained, her voice a little unsteady.

'Really?' His eyes flickered with amusement. 'That should attract a considerable degree of attention.'

'Oh, no—I mean, the figure will have clothes on when I paint it. I just wanted to get the lines of the body right first.'

'I see.'

'I ... didn't realise you were going to be bringing somebody up here,' she managed. 'I wouldn't have ... I mean ...'

'Poor Dirk.' He chuckled. 'It probably hasn't done his blood-pressure a great deal of good.'

'Didn't you mind?' she asked curiously. 'I mean ... well, people might start talking, and what will they think?'

'Perhaps that I am keeping a harem up here?' he suggested with a teasing smile. 'I really do not care what people think. And what was there to talk about, after all? Dirk came upon an artist's model simply doing her job. There was nothing improper about it, unless it was in his own mind.'

He leaned across and flicked over the page to look at the sketch she had done of him. Charlie felt that betraying flush of pink in her cheeks as she waited for him to comment. Would he see the emotions she had been feeling as she had drawn it?

'Hmm. Is that what I look like?' he enquired, a quirk of humour in his voice.

'It's ... just how I saw you at that particular moment. I don't——'

To her enormous relief, the sharp buzz of the telephone interrupted the moment. Piet went to answer it. She heard him say, in English. 'Yes—yes, she is. One moment, I will give her the phone.' She looked up at him enquiringly as he brought it across to her. 'It's your father,' he told her quietly.

Charlie tensed, reluctant to take the phone. But Piet was holding it out to her, and she really had no choice. 'H . . . hello, Daddy,' she managed, her voice shaking.

'So you've reappeared. Kind of you to let me know...I've been worried sick about you for the past few days.'

'Not worried enough to ring sooner to find out if I was OK,' she countered bitterly.

'I've got more important things to do than pander to your foolish behaviour, young lady,' came the brusque response. 'You really have done it this time, haven't you? Supplying drugs, no less! And why didn't you contact me right away? How do you think I felt when I heard that you'd turned to a total stranger for help?'

'I thought perhaps you might have more important things to do,' she put back to him with a heavy irony that she knew would be completely lost on him.

'You were extremely fortunate to find such a reliable friend,' her father went on, as usual more concerned with delivering his lecture than with listening to anything she might have to say. 'I've made a few private enquiries about him, of course, and I have to say that I was extremely pleased. For once you seem to have used a bit of sense. A most respectable young man.'

Charlie closed her eyes for a moment, wishing she could close this scene out of her life altogether. At least Piet couldn't hear what her father was saying.

'Anyway, I'm ringing to let you know that I should be able to spare a few days to come up to Amsterdam next week,' he announced with the satisfaction of knowing that he was doing his paternal duty. 'I shall stay at the Amstel, of course. Perhaps you could bring Meneer Den Ouden to dinner one evening?'

'I'll ask him,' she conceded weakly. The last thing she wanted was for her father to visit, and yet . . . she could never stop herself hoping that this time it would be better, this time he would be a little less disapproving of her, this time they could be like a *normal* father and daughter.

'I'll get my secretary to call you and confirm the arrangements,' he said crisply—she could almost see him checking his engagements diary to see where he could fit her in. 'Goodbye, Charlotte.'

'Goodbye, Daddy,' she murmured wistfully as the line clicked and went dead.

Piet slanted her a look of enquiry.

'He's coming to stay for a few days,' she explained flatly. 'He's invited us both to dinner.'

Piet's grey eyes were lit with understanding as he took the the telephone from her, and set it back on its cradle. 'All right,' he said, nodding. 'It will be . . . interesting to meet him.'

Sir Stafford Heller was not a tall man, and years of living rather well had expanded his waistline. But his personal belief in his own importance carried sufficient weight to impress most people he came into contact with. Thus he had acquired the best table in the restaurant, overlooking the wide sweep of the Amstel River, and was enjoying the most attentive of service.

Charlie had gone to the trouble of buying a dress especially for this occasion—a neat navy blue silk with white polka dots, caught in at her waist with a smart belt and just skimming her knees. The leather handbag and shoes she had bought to go with it were equally conservative. But her father didn't even seem to notice the effort she had made—he was too busy talking international finance with Piet.

'But the fundamental advantage of the free market system,' he was prosing, waving his fork for emphasis, 'is that it will inevitably lead to a much closer relationship between price and the underlying principles of supply and demand.'

'Perhaps,' returned Piet drily. 'Over time, and under laboratory conditions of total non-intervention. But in practice financial markets don't work like that. Dealers make their profits not by getting it right, but by getting in first—they can trade in and out as fast as the blips on their screens will let them.'

'Ah, now that's where the "snake" comes in,' Sir Stafford pointed out with enthusiasm. 'Tactical intervention is all very well—when the impetus of a market is exhausted it can force a trend into reverse. But if governments are really going to be effective they need international agreements to impose some sort of structure.'

'Then that is hardly a free market, is it?'

'But the financial system is essentially different from your other industries...' Sir Stafford paused in his discourse as the waiter brought their coffee. 'Confidence is all. Governments have always regulated thier financial institutions...'

'I think perhaps we are boring Charlie,' Piet commented quietly as she stifled a yawn.

'Oh...!' Her father blinked at her in surprise, as if he had almost forgotten her presence—which she strongly suspected he had. He patted her hand in a patronising gesture that set her teeth on edge. 'I'm sorry, my dear—it's just men's talk. I'd really like an opportunity to discuss this with you further,' he added to Piet. 'The views of the industrial sector are of course a very important consideration. If you are going to be down in Brussels or Strasbourg at any time, perhaps we could have lunch?'

'That would be interesting,' agreed Piet, his voice implying reservations that Charlie was sure her father, satisfied that he was conveying some honour, was unaware of.

'And of course I must thank you for rescuing my daughter from the consequences of her own foolish behaviour. Really, Charlotte, when I think how much I spent on your education . . . !'

'Maybe you should have saved yourself the money and left me with my mother,' she countered, acid on her tongue.

He snorted impatiently. 'Well, you couldn't have turned out much worse!' he declared. 'Getting mixed up with drugs! I suppose you realise the sort of scandal it could have caused if the Press had got hold of it?'

'The drugs were nothing to do with me,' she insisted, her eyes obstinately downcast on the table-cloth. 'They were just on my boat.'

'Well, isn't that enough? It's the kind of friends you choose. If I've told you once, I've told you a thousand times . . .'

'Dad . . .' She slanted Piet an apologetic look. 'Do we really have to wash our dirty linen in public?'

Sir Stafford bestowed a glowing, paternal smile on Piet. 'Well, now, I hardly regard Pieter as public,' he averred. 'After everything he has done I would say he was a friend of the family.'

Charlie could feel her cheeks tingeing a deep pink. In another moment her father would be giving them his blessing—he seemed quite convinced that he had finally found a suitable candidate for her hand in marriage.

'I was glad to have been of assistance,' Piet said, his quiet, even voice lending some sanity to the discussion. 'Your daughter is a very talented artist, sir.'

'Oh . . . well, yes, I suppose she is. I've always given her every encouragement, of course.'

Liar, thought Charlie bitterly, remembering the struggle she had had to persuade him to let her go to art school instead of taking some dire course in interior design he had planned for her.

'So, what's all this about a mural you're painting for Pieter?' he went on jovially. 'Not one of your unintelligible daubs, I hope? I really don't understand all this modern art stuff,' he confided to Piet, fully expecting his agreement. 'I'm sure I can't see what there is in any of it.'

'I believe Charlie is painting a scene of medieval Amsterdam,' Piet responded, somehow managing to subtly take her side without antagonising her father.

'Really? Well, and when am I going to see it?' he enquired, beaming.

Charlie felt a surge of panic. She hated showing any of her paintings to her father—he never, ever liked any of them. 'It . . . it isn't quite finished yet,' she temporised.

He chuckled with laughter. 'Oh, I don't mind that!'

'I . . . don't like people seeing my pictures while I'm still working on them,' she managed, wishing the subject had never been brought up.

'But that doesn't apply to me, surely?' he protested, an edge of annoyance creeping into his tone. 'I am your father, after all.'

She was breathing too fast, her mind a blank as she sought desperately for some excuse that would work.

'I'll come over tomorrow,' he decided. 'I'm really looking forward to seeing it.'

Yes—looking forward to another opportunity to put me down and make me look small, she reflected, acid tears stinging the backs of her eyes. Just as you did to my mother—only she had the option of leaving you. You can't leave your father—you're stuck with him for life.

'Have you finished your coffee, Charlie?' Piet asked gently. 'If so, perhaps it is time for us to go now. Thank you for a most pleasant dinner, sir. I look forward to meeting you again.'

'Of course. Tomorrow morning, yes? I have to leave for Luxembourg by one o'clock.'

The two men rose to their feet, politely shaking hands with each other, and then to Charlie's immense relief Piet took her arm, and led her away from the table. One tear had spilled over and was tracking slowly down her cheek, and she brushed it away fiercely with the back of her hand, not caring that it smudged her mascara.

'I see why your relations with your father are so difficult,' remarked Piet as they stepped outside into the cool night air.

She slanted him a wary look. 'Do you?' she challenged defensively.

'Indeed. He seems intent on fitting you into a mould of his own making, regardless of your natural inclinations. That is always a serious mistake.'

'How would you know?' Contrarily, she didn't want her father criticised—not even by him. 'You've only just met him.'

Piet laughed drily. 'Oh, no—I have known him all my life. He is like my own father in many ways. And in me it produced the same rebellion. The result was that in my youth I ran completely wild, and left all the work of running the business to my brother.'

There was a note in his voice that told her more than he had said. 'You don't—you don't feel guilty about that, do you?' she asked softly.

'Of course I do. It was overwork and stress that killed him. If I had taken on my fair share...'

'But you work much too hard,' she pointed out. 'Every night you don't finish at your desk until after I've gone to bed.'

He laughed wryly. 'Perhaps that is my way of atonement,' he confessed. 'Even though it is too late.'

She tucked her hands into his arm, feeling an instinctive sympathy for him. Linked together like that, they walked the rest of the way home in silence.

CHAPTER EIGHT

'You *what*?' Charlie stared at her father in amazement and growing anger. 'How *could* you?'

Sir Stafford smiled in tolerance at his daughter's outburst. 'I simply spoke to a few important people, pointed out how little foundation there was in the charges. Of course, it was useful to have my contacts—there are certain advantages to my position. I quite understand that it wasn't something that Pieter would be able to do.' He bestowed another benign smile on the young man he hoped would soon be his son-in-law.

'I wouldn't have wanted him to,' Charlie flared, reluctant to even look at Piet while she was quarreling with her father like this. 'How *dared* you interfere? Why couldn't you just leave things alone for once?'

It was his turn to be amazed. 'Oh, now, come, Charlotte—you can't seriously tell me that you *wanted* all this to get dragged into court?'

'Why not? Don't you think I would have got a fair trial? Or do you think I'm guilty?' she challenged furiously.

His brief hesitation revealed a lot, but he tried to cover it by blustering. 'Of course not. I know my daughter would never dream of such a thing—even you know where to draw the line. It's as I explained to the commissar—you're very young, and easily led——'

'Oh, thank you,' she spat. 'It's nice to know that my father thinks of me as some kind of mental defective.'

'I don't think you realise the seriousness of all this, young lady——'

'Perhaps it is best to say that it is done now, for better or worse,' put in Piet in his calm, rational voice. 'I am sure your father acted in the way he thought best, Charlie.' His steady hand on her silenced her bitter protest. 'Just leave it at that, eh?'

Charlie felt herself shaking inside, but she fought to regain her self-control. Piet was right—it was done now, and nothing she could say would undo it. And her father probably had genuinely believed that he had done her a favour—even if his first concern had almost certainly been the possibility of bad publicity that might attach to the case.

Her father too seemed ready to accept the good sense of his words. 'Yes, well ... quite,' he conceded. 'Well, my dear,' he added, glancing at his watch, 'I really have to be getting along soon—I have a plane to catch. Why don't you show me this—er—picture of yours before I go?'

She had to draw a deep breath to steady herself before she could reply. 'It isn't finished yet,' she reminded him, on a last hope that he might give up the idea of seeing it.

'I told you, that doesn't matter,' he insisted complacently. 'I won't mind.'

'Well ... all right, then,' she agreed with a wry reluctance. 'Come on.'

Riding down in the lift, Sir Stafford turned to Piet. 'Very nice little operation you've got here,' he remarked. 'Engineering, mostly, is it?'

Piet nodded. 'Ultra-precision diamond turning and grinding processes mainly.'

Sir Stafford nodded wisely. 'Ah, yes—very much within the sector of the industry that retains a good growth potential. And you've diversified, I suppose?'

'Within the general sphere of our expertise,' Piet allowed. 'We're in optics as well as mechanical components and electronics.'

'Excellent, excellent—I'm sure you're very wise.' They had reached the ground floor, but Sir Stafford seemed more interested in the large open-plan office behind the reception area than in looking at Charlie's mural. Discreetly she remained silent, falling back a little, mentally crossing her fingers that her father would be diverted and would not have time to look at what she had done.

'Would you like to see something of the premises, sir?' Piet invited politely.

'Why, I'd be delighted—if it wouldn't be an intrusion.'

'No intrusion,' Piet assured him. 'Of course, the actual processing takes place in our various factories throughout Europe. But here we have all the development and design facilities—using the latest computer systems, of course—as well as our accounting centre.'

He led the way through into the offices, exchanging the kind of easy greetings with his staff that told Charlie he must be a very good boss to work for. The atmosphere was bright and cheerful, and there was an air of interest and efficiency in the way everyone went about their work.

She was aware that her presence was arousing quite a good deal of curiosity; while she was working on the mural she was hidden behind the dust-sheets, and few of the staff had seen her up close. But it was too late to wish that she hadn't joined the conducted tour; and, besides, she wanted to stay with them—she was afraid of what her father might say to Piet.

In each section a senior member of staff would attatch himself to them, though Piet seemed to know all of his employees and the nature of their work well enough to need no assistance in explaining it all the Sir Stafford. But their talk of transnational company law and European merger regimes was boring for her—she was more interested in watching the antics of the keen young executives in status-rated suits, eagerly vying with each other for an opportunity to impress the boss.

There was quite a little cluster gathered around them by the time they came back to the ground-floor reception area. Charlie had fallen back a little, excluded, and suddenly she found Dirk van Leiden at her side.

'Well, hello!' Those piggy little eyes seemed to crawl all over her, as if he had forgotten that it had been Sara, not her, whom he had seen without any clothes on the other day.

'Hello,' she responded warily.

'So what's all this?' he enquired, that patronising note in his voice grating on her nerves. 'I didn't know Piet was receiving a delegation from the commission today.'

'Oh . . . no.' She shook her head. 'It was just that my father asked if he could have a look around while he was here.'

'Your father?' He blinked in surprise. 'You mean, Sir Stafford? Why, of course!' He beamed widely, showing his yellowed back teeth. 'Heller—I never associated the name. How very remiss of me. I'm sorry.'

She accepted the apology with a slight inclination of her head. Clearly he thought that, as her father's daughter, she was worthy of more respect than some unknown girl who painted pictures. That attitude did nothing to endear him to her.

Her father was beginning to say his goodbyes, and Charlie began to hope that he might have forgotten all about the mural. But she had reckoned without Dirk van Leiden's unnecessary interferences. He had made a point of moving in on her father, reminding him of the last time they had met, slapping him on the back as if he were his oldest friend.

'And what do you think of our new work of art, then, Sir Stafford?' he enquired, gesturing towards the swath of dust-cloths with a wide sweep of his arm.

'Ah, yes! I haven't actually seen it yet.' He looked round as Charlie tried to retreat backwards through a solid wall. 'I only have a moment or two,' he reminded her, as if bestowing a grand favour.

She sighed in weary resignation; she could hardly argue with him here, in front of all these people. Bundling the dust-cloths in her arms, she pulled them down from the rope that suspended them and stood back, refusing to look at the large painting herself, knowing that in its unfinished state it was far from the realisation of the concept she had in her head.

Nobody said very much. There were a few awkward coughs, some clearing of throats. A number of KYEs decided that now was a strategic moment to withdraw, before anything embarrassing might occur. Sir Stafford just stood looking at the scene in puzzled bemusement, tilting his head to first one side then the other, as if trying to make sense of what he could see.

'Is that supposed to be the sky?' he asked at last. 'Why is it that vivid turquoise colour?'

Charlie shrugged one shoulder, casting just a fleeting glance up at her own work. 'It just is, that's all.'

He laughed, disparaging as usual. 'It looks as though a child painted it,' he objected. 'I dont know— you get a splendid opportunity like this to show what you can do, and you just go and throw it away.'

'It isn't finished yet,' she reminded him weakly.

'Three years at art college, to learn to paint like this! I knew it was going to be a waste of money. You should have done as I suggested and taken that course in interior design. At least then you'd have had a qualification you could fall back on. I don't know what Piet thinks of it,' he added, turning to the younger man.

No one could tell—his face was cold and shuttered. 'I'm quite satisfied,' was all he said.

Charlie gazed round at the circle of men, her lower lip quivering as she tried to hold back the tears that were stinging her eyes. 'Well, I'm sorry none of you like it,' she forced out. 'I never pretended to be Graham Rust. And you can always paint over it.' And, dumping the dust-sheets on the floor, she walked right through them, stepping into the private lift and pressing the button for the top floor.

The tears wouldn't come—they were choked by too many years of pain and bitterness. How vividly she could remember, all through her childhood, when she had tried to show him the results of her early artistic efforts, how dismissive he had been. He would always notice if she had got something a little out of proportion, got the perspective wrong. He had his own set ideas about how a painting should look—a kind of idealised photograph—and he never bothered to even try to understand anything else.

The taxi he had ordered was waiting outside, and she watched from the window as he crossed the pavement and stepped into it, attended by the self-important Dirk. She was leaning forward, looking down there for Piet, when the door of the apartment behind her opened, and he came in.

As she stared at him in blank surprise, wondering why he wasn't downstairs seeing her father off, he came across the room in two strides and took her straight into his arms.

'Don't look like that, Charlie—as if all the world has betrayed you,' he begged, kissing the tears from her eyes as they spilled over. 'I know he's your father, but you shouldn't let him cut you up like this.'

'I knew it would be like that,' she sobbed. 'Nobody liked it. And it isn't even finished yet.'

'Hush,' he soothed, stroking her hair. 'Your father might not have liked it, but I did. It's exactly what I wanted—so full of life and joy that it seemed to bounce right out of the wall.'

She lifted her head to look up at him, blinking through her tears as she tried to focus on his face. 'Do you mean that?' she asked warily.

'Of course I mean it. I'm going to chuck that dull old furniture out of the place, and get in something smart and snazzy to go with the picture. And a new carpet, too. In fact, it could give the company a whole new image.'

She laughed shakily. '"Der Ouder's goes to Toy Town"?'

'Why not?' He laughed too, picking her up and swinging her round in his arms. 'Who wants to be an old fuddy-duddy?'

'You *really* like it?' she questioned anxiously. 'You didn't seem very pleased at the time.'

He set her on her feet, looking down at her with serious eyes. 'I was angry with your father,' he said. 'Whether he liked the painting or not, there was no need for him to be so critical, especially with so many other people there.'

'That's why I didn't want him to see it,' she explained wryly. 'Especially not until it was finished. He's never, ever liked anything I've done. Even when I won the prize for my second-year work at college, he couldn't find something nice to say. He just snorted something about what could you expect from people who would pay a fortune for a pile of bricks.'

'You have a very real talent.' Piet's voice was soft and forceful. 'If your father can't see that then that is his loss. I am looking forward to seeing the painting finished. You will finish it, won't you?'

She reached up and wrapped her arms around his neck. 'Oh, of course I will—if you're sure that's what you want.'

'That is what I want,' he said, and his mouth came down to claim hers in a kiss of the deepest tenderness.

She clung to him, her slender body pliant in his arms; when he held her like this nothing else seemed to matter. And as his sensuous tongue explored all the sweetest depths of her mouth she sensed a subtle change in him, a growing tension of male arousal, no longer comforting but demanding.

Her blood heated swiftly, coursing through her veins, and their mouths dragged reluctantly apart as they both sought breath. His hands still held her hard against him, and she could feel the slight rasp of his jaw against her cheek. There was only one thought in her mind, and she reached up on tiptoe to whisper raggedly in his ear, 'Make love to me, Piet.'

For a long moment he seemed to hesitate, and a pain twisted in her heart. Would he reject her again even now? 'Please,' she begged softly, lifting her misted eyes to his. Without a word he scooped her up in his arms, and carried her through into his bedroom.

Sunlight streamed in through muslin curtains. The walls and floor were a plain creamy white, the bed a high-tech four-poster of smooth black steel, covered with a thick duvet of navy, red and white—as cool and uncompromisingly masculine as the man himself. As he laid her down she felt herself suddenly very small and vulnerable. She had asked to come into his lair, and now she was very unsure of what was going to happen. She trusted him, of course, and yet . . . sometimes he could be so much more than she had expected.

But there was no time for doubts or second thoughts. He came down on the bed beside her, half burying her beneath his weight, and his mouth claimed hers in a deep, demanding kiss that warned that her offer had been irrevocably accepted. She struggled to cope, dragging air into her lungs as best she could, desperate with fear that he would find her lack of experience disappointing, after what she had led him to believe.

But oh, the way he kissed! It made her dizzy, just being in his arms like this, feeling the warm strength of his muscles half crushing her, breathing the giddying musky scent of his skin. She had been so focused on that that she hadn't even noticed him unfasten the dozen tiny buttons down the front of her piqué cotton blouse until she felt his hand on her small naked breast.

'Not wearing a bra again,' he growled in her ear, as if she had done it deliberately for his benefit.

Now there were new sensations to focus on as his long, clever fingers cupped and moulded her aching breasts, teasing the tender pink buds of her nipples into a state of raw arousal, so that she moaned softly, arching her back, remembering how it had felt to have his hot mouth there, suckling.

He smiled down at her, his grey eyes heated to a smouldering blue as he filled his gaze with the sight of her naked curves. 'They're perfect,' he murmured softly. 'So small and delicate, and yet your nipples are as red and ripe as raspberries. I want to eat them.' He bent his head, nipping lightly with strong white teeth, making her giggle with delight. 'Mmm—delicious. I want to eat all of you.'

He lifted her in his arms, burrowing into her, covering her shoulders and breasts with gentle, sensuous bites, making peculiar devouring noises that made her laugh, her head tipped back against the pillow. But the laughter was only for a moment—he was too driven by his own urgent hunger to dally in play for long, and soon his mouth was back at her nipples, lapping them with his moist, rasping tongue, suckling deeply.

It was all so new, these delicious sensations so strange. She lay back against the pillow, watching him feast on her body, a little nervous of the power she had unleashed. If he knew this was her first time, would he be a little more gentle? But if she told him that, would he go on? And she wanted him to go on, wanted to give him everything she could offer, wanted to belong to him totally.

He was still wearing his formal grey business suit, and, determined to seem at least a little as if she knew what she was doing, she found enough of her voice to murmur huskily, 'Aren't you even going to take your tie off?'

He laughed, a low, suggestive chuckle, and knelt up, astride her stomach, imprisoning her, a glint of conquering triumph in his eyes as he smiled down at her. With one hand he loosened his tie, a gesture that reminded her with sudden vividness of the way he had removed his tie that first night they had met. It had seemed to her then as though he had been going to take the rest of his clothes off—and now as he shrugged out of his jacket, and began to unbutton his shirt, she watched in a kind of awed fascination.

She had drawn men in life class—she knew what they looked like. But then there had been nothing but a cool, artistic detachment—they had been strangers, meaning nothing to her but a formation of lines and shadows that she was to try to capture on paper with her pencils. But now her heart was pattering at an alarming speed.

He had a beautiful body. She knew every muscle by its scientific name, but as they moved beneath his lightly bronzed skin she felt her mouth grow dry. He was so powerful . . . The sunlight glinted on the scat-

tering of pale gold curls across his wide chest, and
she put up her fingertips to run them through it,
feeling the warm of his body, the strong beat of his
heart.

And then with a smile of unmistakable intent he
put his hand to the waistband of his trousers, and
unclipped it. In a wave of sudden embarrassment, she
closed her eyes, feeling the blush of pink rise to her
cheeks. He moved slightly, and when he came back
into her arms she knew that he had nothing on.

Now he began to strip off the rest of her clothes,
a little impatient. She didn't know whether to help
him or not—she didn't want to seem too forward. It
was all a little scary, and she kept her eyes tightly
closed as she felt him unzip her cotton flowered skirt
and tug it off, pausing only to take off her sandals as
well before turning his attention to her white lace
briefs.

But there was a strange thrill of excitement in lying
there naked on the bed with him. She felt so exquisitely, submissively feminine, defenceless before this
predatory male, and as he ran his hand up possess-
ively over her slender body she quivered in instinctive
response, knowing that there could be no holding
back.

His kisses and caresses were like magic. He seemed
to want to taste every inch of her skin, front and back,
and she moved at his silent commands, wriggling a
little with delight as she lay beneath him, face down
in the pillow, his hands moulding her small breasts as
they were crushed beneath their joint weight, his hot
mouth finding the sensitive hollows at the base of her
throat.

'Mmm—shall I take you like this?' he murmured wickedly. 'From behind, as if you were a bitch on heat?' She gasped in protest, twisting away from him, and he laughed down at her teasingly. 'Haven't you ever done it like that? You don't know what you've been missing. But we can save the exotic stuff for later.' He rolled her on to her back again. 'First I want to take you like this.'

Her breasts were aching and sensitive, and she sobbed on a gasping breath as he subjected them again to his sweet torture. Each nipple was hot and ripe, but he could arouse even sweeter sensations, swirling around them languorously with his tongue, grazing them with his hard teeth, suckling with a deep, pulsing rhythm that made her spine curl in ecstasy.

But she knew this was not all, and as his hand slid slowly up between her thighs, parting them a little, she yielded, trembling. Her heart seemed almost to have stopped beating, but he held her close as he sought the deepest intimacy, the touch of his fingers exquisitely gentle, searching for that most sensitive nub of nerve-endings hidden beneath the moist velvet folds.

She let go her breath on a shuddering sigh, melting in the honeyed tide of warmth that swam through her. Never, ever could she have dreamed it would be like this. It was as if she was caught up in some kind of magic spell that she didn't understand, but could only respond to.

But then Piet seemed to hesitate. 'Charlie?' His voice sounded oddly puzzled.

She opened her eyes to stare anxiously up at him, her heart in a panic that she might have done something wrong.

'Charlie, what is it?' he asked gently. 'If I didn't know better I might almost think...' He paused, gazing down at her as enlightenment slowly dawned. 'I think perhaps you do not have quite the experience you have pretended—is that not so?'

She lowered her lashes, tears filling her eyes. 'Yes,' she whispered forlornly.

'But why then did you say those things? Charlie, tell me.' He was cradling her in his arms, stroking her hair. 'Why did you wish me to believe that you were so promiscuous?'

'I...I don't know. I think it was because I was afraid. Because I was falling in love with you.'

'Oh, Charlie...' His warm lips kissed away her tears again.

'Piet, please.' Somehow she forced herself to lift her eyes to his. 'Make love to me. I...I want you to.'

He smiled, stroking his fingertips gently down over her cheek. 'Are you a virgin, Charlie?' he asked.

She could only nod, her throat too constricted for words, all that she wanted to say expressed in her eyes. For a long moment he seemed to consider, and she felt a growing dread that he would refuse, that this wonderful thing that had started would end in empty nothingness.

But then he conceded a wry laugh, almost an admission of defeat. Gently he drew her thighs apart. 'You realise that now you are going to have to marry me, don't you?' he murmured, a strange note, maybe even of mockery, in his voice.

She blinked at him, bewildered, searching his face. 'But...why?' she whispered faintly.

He smiled, a strange smile that she didn't quite understand. 'You don't think I'm ever going to let

you go, do you?' he queried, shifting to lie above her.
'You belong to me—I want exclusive rights, signed,
sealed and delivered. I have hated every man I thought
had been like this with you, and now that I know
there have been none before me I intend to make very
sure that there are no others.'

Her mind was in a turmoil of confusion. But she
wasn't sure if that sounded like a proper reason to get
married. But how could she possibly refuse, when she
loved him so desperately, when to be married to him—
whatever his reasons—was all the happiness she could
ever ask for?

Somehow she managed to find her voice, gazing up
into the fathomless depths of those hypnotic grey eyes.
'Yes,' she whispered. 'Oh, yes, Piet, I'll marry you,
if that's what you want.'

He nodded, satisfied, and with one smooth,
powerful thrust took possession.

She gave a little gasp as she felt her body yield, but
there was no real pain. He paused, as if to allow her
a little time to adjust, and then began to move with
a slow, deep rhythm, stirring an odd little sensation
of pleasure inside her.

'You like this?' he asked, gently teasing.

'Oh, yes...'

'There is much, much more.' His voice was low and
husky with sensual promise. 'Your days of rebellion
are over, young lady. From now on, if you defy me
I will know exactly how to bring you under control.'

'How?' she challenged, her eyes wide with mischievous innocence.

'Like this.'

It was like riding on the wings of a storm, wild and
dangerous. As the driving rhythm grew stronger she

began to move with him, offering her fragile body willingly to the force of his demand. Some deep, animal hunger was stirring inside her, matching his, and she moaned softly as the pleasure inside her mounted. They were both breathing raggedly, gasping for air, their bodies slicked with sweat, and she arched beneath him, clinging to him, her fingernails raking his back.

In his urgency he seemed to have forgotten her innocence, but it no longer mattered. The flames rose around her, forging her love like the purest, strongest diamond into her heart, until with a last wild cry she felt herself falling, clinging to him, crushed in his arms as the tumult exploded through them both and died away, fading at last into quiet and sunlight and white muslin curtains drifting on the summer breeze.

CHAPTER NINE

THE diamond on Charlie's finger was huge. She moved her hand, capturing the rays of the sun within it, fascinated by the flare of fire at its heart. Beside her at the wheel of the big, comfortable Mercedes, Piet laughed softly. 'You like it?'

'It's beautiful!' She smiled up at him in blissful happiness. 'I can hardly believe this is really happening.'

'It's happening,' he assured her, smiling back. 'I think perhaps my mother was even more surprised than your father.'

'Oh, he'd already decided it was an excellent idea—you're just the type he always wanted me to marry,' she told him teasingly. 'At least for once in my life I've managed to do something to please him.'

The road was straight and clear, and Piet took one hand off the wheel to cover hers. 'I hope it will improve the understanding between you, then,' he said. 'It is sad that father and daughter should be so estranged.'

'Yes.' Her expression changed to one of wry apprehension. 'I just hope your mother approves as much of your choice,' she added nervously. 'She might think you're getting the thin end of the bargain.'

His grey eyes danced with amusement. 'Ah, she knows me far too well to think that,' he assured her. 'It may take her a little time to grow accustomed to the idea, but I'm sure she will like you very much.'

143

'I hope so.' She gazed out of the window at the passing landscape. On each side of the road the flat, level fields stretched to the low horizon; only an occasional steep-roofed house or stand of trees broke the skyline, or here and there a white wooden drawbridge spanning one of the arrow-straight ditches that divided up the fields into neat rectangles.

They were on their way to visit Piet's mother. On his father's death she had returned to live in the village where she had grown up, not very far from Amsterdam, on the edge of the calm grey IJ. As soon as Piet had telephoned and told her of his engagement, she had insisted that they should come up for Sunday lunch.

The news must have come as quite a surprise to her, Charlie reflected ruefully. She had never heard of this English girl her son was seeing—and suddenly he was announcing his engagement! What must she be thinking? *Would* she approve of his choice?

She was wearing the same navy and white silk dress she had worn for her father, and had made a real effort to control her wild curls, brushing them until they shone, and confining them back from her face with a twisted scarf of navy silk that matched her dress. At least the colour suited her, flattering the blue of her eyes.

It really was very hard to believe that this could be happening, that she was engaged to Piet. Perhaps it was too soon yet—it was only three days since he had asked her. Maybe she just needed a little more time to get used to it.

But why *had* he asked her? Even at the time, that question had whispered at the back of her brain. Surely it couldn't simply be that he felt it was his duty, since he had taken her virginity? Even *he* wasn't old-fashioned enough for that. And yet...he hadn't actually said that he loved her. She had been so overjoyed at the possibility of marrying him that she had made herself ignore that niggling little omission. But *should* she ignore it?

Covertly she cast him a glance from beneath her lashes. He seemed totally intent on driving the car—she might almost just as well not be there. It had been a little like that for the past three days—if she had been expecting him to forget all about his business responsibilities, and lavish all his time and attention on her, she would have been sadly disappointed.

Of course, when he was with her, it was wonderful. They had made love as if it had just been invented—which for her, of course, it had. But for him...well, there was no mistaking that degree of experience, or expertise. How many other women had there been in his life? Apart from that redhead, of course...Janine.

A small frown furrowed her brow at the memory of the beautiful Frenchwoman. Somehow there seemed to be something not quite right there. She was honest enough with herself to know that, though she was reasonably pretty, she was no match for that chic, elegant creature, who seemed to be so much more Piet's type.

Why had he chosen to marry her, instead of Janine? True, he hadn't seemed unduly troubled when his relationship with her had come to such an abrupt end; what was it he had said? That it wasn't a relationship in the sense she had meant. What exactly had he meant by that?

These worries were still with her as they left the *autokade*, turning off at a roundabout to drive down

a narrower two-lane country road. A canal ran
alongside the road, and ahead rose the steep red roofs
of a small village, half hidden among the shady trees
that surrounded it.

But Piet turned off before they reached it, crossing
the canal by a narrow bridge and taking the lane that
ran along its other bank. After a moment they came
to a low stone wall, and behind it Charlie could see
a substantial house of light reddish brick, with the
traditional steeply pitched roofs and stepped gables
of most Dutch houses. A wrought-iron gate gave entry
to a neatly kept garden, bright with roses.

'Here we are.' Piet drew the car to a halt on the
immaculate gravel drive, and climbed out to come
round and open her door for her with his usual precise
attention to gentlemanly manners. She stepped out,
and looked up at the house with interest.

Now that she could see it more closely, she recognised that it was quite old. It had several wings, added
possibly at different times but in the same style,
making interesting angles in the line of the roof. The
windows of the two lower floors were unusual, the
upper halves leaded, the lower covered in varnished
wooden shutters, which all stood open to the summer
sun. And the front door was of ancient polished oak,
solid and imposing.

But, as they walked towards the three stone steps
that led up to it, it was thrown open, and a plump,
middle-aged lady with fluffy light brown hair greeted
them with a beaming smile and a flow of Dutch that
Charlie couldn't follow—she spoke the language only
slightly.

Piet answered her in English. 'Thank you, Hannie—
I'm fine. And this is Charlie. Charlie—my Aunt

Hannie. She lives here with my mother, and looks after her.'

'Oh.' She had thought for a brief moment that this *was* his mother, but she had quickly guessed that the lady was rather too young. *'Goedemorgen,'* she said politely.

Hannie had returned that look of surprise—Charlie guessed that she was thinking that *she* was too young, too. But her smile was warm. 'Ah, how nice to meet you. Do come inside. Mevrouw Der Ouder is in the garden—go through, and I will bring out some coffee, *ja*?'

'Thank you, Hannie.'

Inside the house was elegantly furnished; the Dutch antiques tended to be large and heavy, but they blended perfectly with the big, square wood-panelled rooms. And that was a real Vermeer above the carved stone fireplace, Charlie knew at once.

The garden was reached through a pair of french windows that stood wide open. Outside was a stone-flagged terrace, with steps leading down to a well tended lawn, surrounded by neat flowerbeds. Beneath a shady lime tree had been set out some deck-chairs, and in one of them an older woman sat reading.

She was past middle age, but not yet elderly, dressed more for comfort than fashion, but even so with a subtle air of elegance. She glanced up as she heard them come out of the house—and Charlie was sure she could detect a hint of a frown.

But her greeting to her son was warm. 'Ah, my dear—there you are!' She put out both her hands, and Piet took them as he bent to kiss her cheek.

'Mother, I want you to meet my fiancée,' he said, drawing Charlie forward.

'Oh, yes.' Charlie felt herself the subject of a comprehensive scrutiny, and had the uncomfortable feeling that she didn't meet with the fullest approval. 'Good morning, my dear.' There was just a little stiffness in her words. 'I'm delighted to meet you.'

'How do you do?' Charlie responded, managing a shy smile.

'Won't you sit down?'

Charlie murmured a word of thanks, perching very upright in one of the deckchairs, her hands clasped tensely in her lap. It was all so awkward and formal, and Mevrouw Den Ouden seemed as relieved as she was herself when Hannie came out with the coffee.

'Ah, Hannie—excellent. Pieter, fetch that low table over so that Hannie may set down the tray.'

In the flurry of arranging everything there seemed some easing of the constraint. Charlie accepted a cup from Hannie and a square of the sweet, dark Friesian cake, glad at least of something to do with her hands. When they were all settled again Mevrouw Den Ouden turned to her, dutifully opening the conversation.

'My son tells me that you paint,' she remarked with polite interest.

'Yes.' Charlie's response was a little apprehensive—she was not very confident that her career would commend her to her future mother-in-law.

'I am looking forward to seeing this mural when it is finished. I confess, I find it a little hard to imagine, from Pieter's description. But then, I am not very familiar with modern art.'

'Oh, it isn't an abstract,' Charlie assured her quickly. 'It's just . . . I like to use bright colours.'

'I see.'

There was an uncomfortable lull in the conversation. Charlie sipped her coffee and nibbled nervously at her cake, wishing a little desperately that her usual easy flow of small talk had not chosen this day to totally desert her.

'I . . . This is very nice cake,' she managed. 'Is it home-made?'

'No, dear—I buy it from a little baker's in the village,' Hanni told her, smiling with a kindliness that seemed to recognise how difficult she was finding this visit. 'But he makes it right there in his shop. I've been buying from him for years. He's very good.'

'Yes, he is.' Charlie flickered her a grateful smile.

That silence stretched again, and at last Piet's mother suggested, 'Would you like to see the garden, my dear? Pieter will show you around.'

'Thank you—I'd love to.' Charlie seized on the offer at once, glad of any excuse to pass the time.

'Lunch will be ready in half an hour. Have a nice stroll.' By her smile, Charlie knew that the older woman too had been feeling the strain.

The garden was charming. Wide grassy paths wound between beds of flowering shrubs and shady trees, running down to the banks of the canal, where soft reeds whispered in the summer breeze. Brightly coloured butterflies were dancing around the lilac flower-spikes of a buddleia, and a greenfinch was singing his warbling song from the branches of a willow that dipped its branches gracefully into the slow-moving waters of the canal.

'What a lovely place!' Charlie remarked sincerely.

Piet smiled down at her. 'I'm glad you like it. I often come out here at weekends, to get away from the noise of the town.'

'Oh.' And, of course, now he would be expecting her to come with him. 'Your mother... I'm not sure if she likes me,' she mumbled, watching abstractedly as a small family of moorhens scudded in and out among the reeds.

'I told you, she may take a little time to get used to you,' he reminded her evenly. 'She is, after all, almost seventy, and she has not been very accustomed to meeting strangers these past few years.'

'No.' And maybe she had been expecting him to marry someone else, she reflected ruefully. Someone older, more suitable...

Piet put his hand under her chin, tilting up her face. 'You will give her time?' he asked seriously. 'I am quite sure she will come to like you once she knows you.'

She managed a tremulous smile—how could anything else matter, when he looked at her like that? 'Of course I'll give her time,' she whispered. 'I want her to like me.'

'Good.' His mouth brushed lightly over hers, and her lips parted in instinctive response, inviting one of his deep, tender kisses. He drew her into his arms, and for a long, long time they were both lost to all other thoughts.

But at last Piet lifted his head, and glanced at his watch. 'I think we should return now to the house,' he said. 'Lunch will be ready in just a few moments.'

Charlie had to draw a deep, slow breath, and struggle to steady the wild racing of her heart. How was it that he could seem so cool, she wondered with a shred of resentment, when even such a relatively chaste kiss could create such a fevered havoc inside her?

He held her hand as they walked back up to the house. His mother had gone inside, and as they crossed the terrace into the comparative cool of the living-room, their footsteps silenced by the thick Aubousson carpet that lined the floor, they heard the sound of her voice from across the hall.

She was speaking in Dutch, and Charlie didn't speak enough of the language to know exactly what was being said, but she did catch—quite distinctly—the name Janine. She stiffened, casting a covert glance up at Piet from beneath her lashes to see his reaction.

He looked faintly annoyed, and to warn of their presence cleared his throat loudly. At once his mother called out, 'Ah, Pieter, is that you? Lunch is ready.' She came through from the dining-room, looking a little self-conscious, as if knowing she had been overheard and not sure how much Charlie might have understood. 'Did you enjoy the garden, my dear?' she enquired, clearly trying to be friendly.

'Yes, thank you.' Charlie murmured, wishing she could just run away. She didn't know for sure, but she could guess, that Mevrouw Den Ouden would have preferred that her son should have married the eminently more suitable Janine. And she herself would very much like to know why he hadn't.

The rest of the afternoon could not be described as anything other than awkward. The conversation during lunch was stilted, and it was clearly a relief to everyone when, at the earliest possible opportunity, Piet suggested that it was time to leave.

As they drove back to Amsterdam the atmosphere of the afternoon still seemed to linger between them. Charlie would have liked to ask him about Janine, but she didn't quite know how. So she sat silent, brooding over her own doubts and anxieties, wondering what he was thinking as he handled the wheel skilfully.

Why had he asked her to marry him? They couldn't be more different—and those thirteen years between their ages couldn't be denied. Had he already been having difficulties in his relationship with Janine before she had arrived on the scene? Was he 'on the rebound' in some way? Maybe Janine had resented being spared so little of his time and attention—if he had always devoted so much of it to his business affairs as he had these past few weeks—and they had been quarreling.

Maybe he thought a younger girl, who adored him to distraction, would be easier to train to be less demanding. Especially when just one kiss, just one touch of his hand could reduce her in seconds to a state of helpless defencelessness. She would be happy to keep his bed warm for him, and ask for little else.

Was that how he meant it to be? A heavy sadness lay in her heart. She didn't want to be relegated to just one little corner of his life; she wanted to share all of it, to understand his business worries, to help him in any way she possibly could. That just went to show how much she loved him, she reflected wryly— she had always hated any discussion of business and finance.

But if she tried to push herself into areas where he didn't want her she could risk losing what she had. He might decide that she was being a nuisance, and

get rid of her. She would have to be careful, per-
suading him at first just to spend a little more time
with her. Surely even *he* needed to relax now and then?
She could start by helping him to do that.

The campaign got off to a slow start. There was a
special exhibition at the Van Gogh Museum, of
paintings on loan from one of the museums in Paris,
and Piet agreed willingly enough to go with her; but
Charlie soon found that getting him to say exactly
when he would be able to spare the time was much
more difficult.

'Wednesday afternoon—I promise,' he vowed, but
then a crisis in a major contract with the Italian
government cropped up at the last minute. 'Friday
morning—I have a meeting at nine, but I will certainly be free by eleven, and we can have the rest of
the day together.'

But then the meeting dragged on, and had to be
followed by urgent talks with the bank, and then he
couldn't go out because he had to wait for a vital call
from   Japan.   Charlie   couldn't   hide   her
disappointment.

'I am truly sorry, Charlie,' he sighed, slipping his
arm around her waist and drawing her against him.
'But this is important.'

She pouted to let him see how upset she was. 'Aren't
I important?' she protested.

'Of course you are.' He dropped a light kiss on the
tip of her nose. 'We shall go as soon as I can get
away. The gallery does not close until five.'

'But it's almost half-past three now— I don't want
to have to rush around and not see anything properly,'
she argued.

'We will go as soon as we can.'

The firm note in his voice was unmistakable, and reluctantly she let the subject drop. They finally got to the exhibition on Saturday afternoon. But the wait had been worth it; Charlie was entranced by the incredible works—the vivid richness of the painting of the church at Auvers, the tortured emotions poured on to the canvas in the picture of the cottages at Cordeville, the swirling despair of the last self-portrait.

She stood gripping Piet's hand, wondering at the sheer genius of a man who could produce such extraordinary richness. And afterwards they went to visit the house on the Prinsengracht where the little Jewish girl Anne Frank had hidden with her family during the later years of the war and had written her diaries; and she stood gripping Piet's hand again as she gazed at the film-star pictures pasted so poignantly to the wall, wondering with silent tears in her eyes at the insanity and hatred that could murder a fifteen-year-old girl.

'She wasn't even as old as me,' she whispered as they turned away.

Piet slipped his arm comfortingly around her shoulders, resting his cheek for a moment against her hair, and she knew without his having to say anything that he shared her thoughts.

Leaving that haunting place behind, they walked down to the Rokin, and climbed aboard one of the glass-topped tour-boats for a trip around the canals. The evening shadows were falling softly around them as they cruised slowly beneath the bridges, each one brightly lit up, casting its mirror image on to the dancing waters below. They sipped wine as Piet pointed out the most interesting sights—the place where she could see the spans of seven bridges all in a row, receding into the distance, and then around the corner the graceful wooden Magere Bridge spanning the wide Amstel River.

By then her wistful mood had lifted, and to make her laugh he took her for a stroll through the busy red-light district, with all its noise and life and colour. She had walked through here quite often during the day, but never at night before, and it made her giggle to see the throngs of tourists goggle-eyed at the blatant advertisements outside the nightclubs, or trying to pretend not to stare at the girls behind the windows.

'They're all so matter-of-fact about it,' she remarked, bemused. 'Not like in England, where it's all hidden away in the dark.'

Piet shrugged, slanting her a look of wicked amusement. 'It's just business,' he pointed out.

'Hmm! I saw Dirk van Leiden here the other day,' she added, remembering.

'Dirk?' He looked puzzled. 'What was he doing here?'

'Oh, just walking along.' She felt a little uncomfortable; she hadn't meant to imply that Dirk had been here for any more suspect reason than she herself. 'It was when I was sketching ideas for the mural,' she added. 'We walked back together.'

'Oh…' He let the subject drop, and they wove their way through the crowds on the pavement, having to concentrate on every step on the uneven cobbles, between the cars passing too quickly for the narrow way and the dangerous unguarded drops into semi-basements.

At last they reached the quiet of the inner harbour, and Charlie stood gazing out over the busy waterway, letting the cool breeze from the Ijsselmeer ruffle her hair, her imagination picturing how it must have been to stand here before the artificial islands opposite them had existed, before the great nineteen-mile Afsluitdijk had enclosed the Zuyder Zee, and all this had been open to the cruel North Sea.

'This is where the ships would have sailed from, isn't it?' she mused quietly. 'It must have been strange to see them go, and know that they wouldn't be back for maybe a year or more. And yet now we can fly to the other side of the world in half a day!'

Piet laughed. 'Ah, yes—the world is definitely a much smaller place. And that is just as well— I could not spare a year for a voyage if I had to visit one of my factories in Jakarta.'

'No!' She shuddered at the thought of having to let him go for so long, wrapping both her arms tightly around his waist and holding him close.

He smiled down at her. 'Ah, my little Charlie—you are so cross that I must spend so much time on my business, and have not the time to go walking through the park with you. Whatever would you have done if you had had to stand here and wave goodbye to me, like the lady on the Weeping Tower?'

'I wouldn't have let you go,' she insisted fiercely. 'But it isn't just because I want you to walk in the park with me. I worry about you.' She looked up at him seriously. 'You work much too hard. You've built up your companies—why can't you let them take care of themselves now, and take some time to enjoy yourself?'

'Ah, if only it were that easy!' He shook his head. 'In business there is no such thing as standing still. That would mean inevitably to fall back as others pressed forward to overtake. Always there must be new moves, innovation, always to stay ahead of the competition.'

'It sounds like some kind of monster, taking over your life,' she protested.

He smiled wryly. 'Yes—in a sense it is,' he admitted. 'I work for a year, only to make for myself another two years' work. It seems that I cannot escape.'

'You could if you really wanted to. You could sell the company.'

Charlie caught her breath as soon as she had said it. It hadn't been planned—the idea had just slipped into her head, and she had blurted it out without thinking. She knew at once that she had made him angry—his body stiffened, and abruptly he let her go.

'It is not to be considered,' he rapped, turning to walk around the headland towards the Damrak. 'I have no wish to be idle.'

She ran to catch up to his side. 'I didn't mean just to give up working completely, and do nothing,' she argued, desperate to avoid a quarrel. 'But there are surely so many other things you'd like to do with your life, besides working yourself to death?'

He stopped suddenly, turning to face her, his eyes hard and cold. 'Do not even talk of such things,' he grated. 'The company was my father's life, and my brother's, and now it is mine.'

'It *took* their lives,' she cried, suddenly recognising that the challenge was bigger than she had ever anticipated. 'And it'll take yours if you're not careful.'

'Hard work never killed anybody,' he countered harshly.

'It does,' she whispered. 'The kind of overwork and stress you put yourself through. Why? Why do you do it? You can't change what happened to your brother. You're just being stupid!'

'It is something I do not wish to discuss with you,' he rapped, turning to walk on.

'Why not?' She was desperate now. 'I'm your fiancée.'

'Quite. And you knew when you accepted my proposal how hard I have to work to pay for things like that very large diamond on your finger. So please do not start complaining now.'

'I'm not complaining . . .'

But he wasn't listening. He had walked on, leaving her to follow after him or go her own way, whatever she wished. And that was how it was going to be, she reflected bitterly. He had made it quite clear that there were vast areas of his life on which she must not intrude. If she wanted to be with him she would have to be content with whatever crumbs he was willing to spare.

But she wanted to be with him so much that she knew she would accept his terms. She would always be there, whenever he wanted her, in the little cracks of time between the obviously more important aspects of his life. She would warm his bed and make him smile, and never demand more than he was willing to give. Even though he still hadn't said he loved her.

CHAPTER TEN

'ARE you *really* sure you're happy, Charlie?'

Charlie laughed, tossing her wild blonde curls around her shoulders. 'Of course I am, Duncan. Life's absolutely wonderful—how can you even ask?'

'Well...I just can't imagine you being engaged—especially to a man like that. I mean...well, he's so...'

Charlie punched her old friend playfully on the chest. 'Don't say another word!' she warned him, making her eyes dance to hide the shadows in them. 'Besides, Piet isn't what you'd expect from the way he looks. He's...exciting, and generous, and fun to be with, and...oh, I just can't explain!'

Duncan smiled wryly. 'All right—I get the message. He's Superman and Father Christmas all rolled into one. Well, I can only wish you happy, love. Just don't forget your old friends if you need us.'

'Thanks, Dunc.' She glanced up as the clear carillon bells of the Munttoren told the half-hour. 'Anyway, I'd better be going. I'm going to try my hand at making a cake today.'

'Making a cake? You?' He stared at her in surprise. 'Hey, don't you think you're taking this domestic bit a little too far? What's happened to the old Charlie, who couldn't boil an egg?'

'I could boil an egg!' she protested, laughing. 'And I am still the old Charlie. It's just that...well, I'm getting married. You wouldn't expect me to stay exactly the same, would you?'

159

'Hmm.' Duncan looked doubtful. 'I just hope this Piet of yours isn't trying to force a round peg into a square hole, that's all.'

'It's a square peg,' she corrected him, leaning over to drop a fond kiss on his cheek. 'And he isn't, I promise. 'Bye, Duncan. See you around.'

She pushed away on her bike, her feet finding the pedals, pausing at the corner to let a rattling yellow tram go by. It was a lovely sunny day, the clear blue sky reflecting in the dancing waters of the canals. How could anyone possibly have doubts or anxieties on a day like this?

Besides, how could she have any doubts? She was in love, she was engaged to be married—Piet's diamond was sparkling on her finger to prove it. The fact that he was already married—to his work—was a minor problem. Many women had to cope with far worse.

Steering carefully between the traffic, she turned into the Herengracht and drew up outside the lofty Der Ouder building. Its imposing grandness was still rather inclined to intimidate her, even though her colourful mural had now completely transformed the reception area—she could see it through the window as she bent to padlock her bicycle to the railings outside.

She had finished it two days ago, and she was actually rather proud of it. It still puzzled her a little why Piet had wanted her to paint something so out of keeping with the usual dignified elegance of the offices, but that was up to him...

'Why, Miss Heller—good morning. Here, let me give you a hand with your shopping.'

She turned sharply, recognising the smooth voice of the diamond merchant, Dirk van Leiden. She had never been able to make herself like the man, and now she moved instinctively away from him, forcing a smile. 'Oh . . . no, thank you—I can manage,' she insisted edgily. 'Thank you.' She lifted her bags from the basket on the bicycle, trying to pretend that they weren't heavy.

'Ah, of course—the liberated modern miss, so independent.' He chuckled, smiling down at her like a kindly uncle. 'I saw you round the corner, talking to your friend,' he added, a little too blandly. 'I would have stopped and offered my assistance then, but . . . it seemed that your attention was fully engaged.'

Charlie eyed him with wary distaste—somehow he had managed to make her innocent conversation with Duncan sound like some kind of guilty secret. And she couldn't miss that lustful glint in his piggy little eyes every time he looked at her. She knew exactly what he was thinking. Maybe she ought to talk to Piet about it . . . But he had enough to worry about at the moment—he hadn't discussed it with her, but she knew there was a problem with export guarantees on a big contract with Thailand.

Letting herself into the hall, she pressed the button to open the lift doors, and stepped inside. Almost at once she had the disturbing sensation that something was wrong. That perfume lingering on the air . . . Expensive, French—it wasn't one she ever wore. Her heart thudded as the association sprang instantly into her mind—red hair, a chic elegance . . . Janine.

No—she was jumping to conclusions. Janine wasn't the only woman who wore that perfume. And even if she *had* been here, there would be an innocent explanation—Piet would tell her about it. She ought to trust him, and not start letting her imagination run away with her—it was just her own insecurity.

The apartment was empty when she let herself into it, and that perfume lingered here too—even in the bedroom. But she refused to allow herself to dwell on the question it presented; instead she went into the kitchen and unpacked her shopping, and then, opening the new cook-book she had bought herself a few days before, she began to measure out the ingredients for her cake, concentrating intently.

She was in the middle of whipping up the eggs when the door opened, and Piet came in. 'Oh!' she protested in laughing disappointment. 'You weren't supposed to come up yet— I wanted this to be a surprise for you.'

'What is this?' He came into the kitchen, coming up close behind her and wrapping his arms around her waist from behind.

'I'm making a cake.'

'Ah! All this, for one cake?' He cast his eye along the worktop, which was littered with flour and currants and used spoons and forks.

'Well, I'm not very good at it yet,' she explained. 'It's the first one I've ever made.'

'And I have to eat it?' He pulled a horrified face, teasing her.

'Of course. I'm going to be a perfect wife—once I've had a bit of practice.'

He laughed, low and smoky, his breath warm against her ear. 'I have a better idea,' he murmured. 'We will send out for cakes, and instead you will practise the wifely talents that you are best at.' He let his hands slide up beneath her loose cotton T-shirt to mould her small, ripe breasts. 'These talents you are very, very good at.'

'Piet . . . !' Her voice was shaky as his palms rasped over the tender buds of her nipples. He could arouse her so easily; but the memory of that French perfume still tugged at her mind, and she struggled to resist. 'I'm making a cake,' she protested, playing for time.

He bent his head to swirl his tongue into the sensitive little hollow behind her ear. 'Come to bed,' he coaxed, expertly inciting her body into a state of helpless arousal.

Her head tipped back against his shoulder, and she felt her spine melting like warm honey. But she needed to know the truth first. 'Were you up here earlier?' she asked carefully.

'Up here?' There was an oddly evasive note in his voice. 'Why should I have been up here?'

'Oh, I . . . just wondered.' She slanted him a searching look from beneath her lashes. 'Were you?'

His face was closed. 'I have been in a very boring business meeting all morning,' he responded, as blankly as a brick wall. His voice became a husky growl. 'And all I could think of was the things I was going to do to you as soon as I could get away,' he added, demonstrating by teasing and plucking at her nipples in an erotic torment, knowing exactly how sensitive they were to such treatment.

But her brain was troubled by uncomfortable suspicions; if the explanation for Janine's presence was innocent, why hadn't he told her? And now he was deliberately trying to distract her. She shook her head, her mind struggling to deny the treacherous arousal of her body.

'No, Piet,' she protested weakly. 'I'm making a cake.'

His grey eyes lit with sudden anger. 'Spare me such a transparent excuse,' he rapped. 'You are being stupid and childish because I haven't spent enough time with you. You must learn to be less selfish—I cannot spend every hour of the day dancing attendance on you.'

'I'm not——'

'Damn your cake!' he grated, and before she had time to realise what he was going to do he had lifted her over his shoulder and was carrying her through to the bedroom.

'Piet—put me down!' she gasped in angry shock.

He did—on to the bed, coming down on top of her and trapping her beneath his weight. 'This is the only wifely talent I am interested in,' he taunted, capturing both her wrists in one strong hand and pinning them back above her head. 'Anybody can bake a cake.'

He lifted her skirt, and without even bothering to strip off her lace french knickers he took her with a fierce thrust of pent-up hunger, as if they hadn't spent the whole of last night making love. Part of her revelled crazily in this proof of just how much he wanted her, but another part was rebelling at his attitude that she was there solely for his pleasure, whether she liked it or not.

Her anger lent a fierce edge to her response, and it was a growling, snarling coupling, swift and savage, ending on a wild animal cry from both of them as they fell in a tangled heap in each other's arms, panting raggedly for breath.

Piet rose quickly to his feet, smiling down at her in glittering amusement as she lay sprawling and dishevelled across the bed. 'Don't try to pretend that you didn't want that,' he taunted scornfully. 'You were as willing as you always are.'

She glared up at him in hot fury. 'That's all you want me for, isn't it?' she threw at him. 'You might as well have one of the girls from down on *walletjes*.'

'Do not talk such foolishness,' he countered sharply. 'I do not have time for one of your silly quarrels now—I have an important meeting this afternoon.'

'Well, you'd better get back downstairs, then, hadn't you?' she retorted, her voice edged with bitterness. 'And I can finish my cake.'

He laughed in dry mockery. 'As you wish.' And with that he was gone, straightening the tie that he hadn't even bothered to remove. She swore furiously as she heard the front door close behind him, grabbing the pillow and hurling it across the room. He had treated her like...like some kind of street tart, not the woman he was engaged to marry. And, in doing so, he had avoided having to answer any awkward questions about Janine.

Rage and jealousy boiled up inside her like a firestorm. What the hell was going on? Why was he still seeing that woman? He had tried to deny their relationship before, but, if it had been as he had said, why had she been so furiously angry to find another woman installed in his apartment? Was he hoping to have his bread buttered on both sides—a wife *and* a mistress? But if that was the case, why was he bothering to get married at all?

Frustrated for any other outlet for her emotions, she took them out on the cake, beating the mixture to within an inch of its life. She had just finished, and was spooning it out into the baking dish, when there was a rap on the door. Curious, she went to open it, to find Dirk van Leiden standing there, an apologetic smile on his round face.

'Ah—I am so sorry to trouble you. Might I come in for just a moment? There are some papers I require—I could not disturb Pieter, as he is in a most important meeting.'

'Oh... yes, of course.' She held the door wider, stepping back to let him pass.

He glanced around as he stepped into the room. 'You are not painting today?'

Charlie almost had to smile at the shadow of disappointment in his voice. 'No, not today,' she responded. 'As a matter of fact, I was making a cake.'

'A cake?' His eyes lit up. 'Ah, but I love homemade cake.'

She laughed. 'I'm afraid it isn't ready yet— I was just about to put it into the oven.'

'You have the baking mix? May I have a taste?' He chuckled. 'A childish habit, I know, but I find it irresistible.'

'Of course.' With a smile she invited him into the kitchen, and he made a beeline for the bowl, dipping in with a greedy finger to scrape out a scoop of the sweet mixture from the side.

'Ah, delicious!' he approved. 'Pieter is a very lucky man.'

She couldn't quite hide the wry frown that crossed her face, and he noticed it at once.

'There is something wrong?' he asked in anxious concern.

'Oh... no.' She lifted one shoulder in a dismissive shrug. 'Not really.'

'Are you sure?' His voice was surprisingly gentle, and she could feel the suppressed tears welling up inside her.

'It's just . . . he always seems to be working,' she explained, wishing to give away no more than the bare minimum. 'I don't seem to see very much of him sometimes.'

Dirk nodded in sympathetic understanding. 'Ah, yes. I am afraid the company must always come first with him. That is why I was a little surprised . . .'

He broke off abruptly, and she glanced up at him in question. 'Surprised at what?'

He looked a little awkward, as if he would have preferred not to answer. 'That he would have chosen . . . someone so young for a wife,' he conceded at last. 'It seemed to me that it would have been more sensible . . .'

'If he had married someone older,' she completed for him. 'Someone a little more mature and sophisticated.' His embarrassment told her that she was on the right track. 'Someone like his French mistress, for instance?' He tried to splutter some sort of answer, but she saved him the bother. 'I know she was here today.'

He stared at her in amazement. 'He *told* you?'

'No.' So it was true! Her heart was twisting in pain. 'But I know.'

He put his arm comfortingly around her shoulders. 'I would have warned you sooner, but I was not sure.' He offered her his handkerchief as she began to cry. 'It pains me to see you hurt like this. I wish there was something I could do.' He stroked her hair soothingly.

'I don't understand why he asked me to marry him if he wants to go on seeing her,' she sobbed brokenly. 'It doesn't make any sense.'

'Ah, but I'm afraid it does,' he murmured, drawing her into his arms. 'Your father, you see—he has the power to do Den Ouden's a great deal of good.' She stared up at him, aghast, and he nodded. 'A little assistance with regional aid grants here, a little push to obtain special concessions there...'

'Oh, no...!' But she knew he was right, and the whole bottom seemed to have dropped out of her world. What a fool she had been—what a naïve, deluded little fool! She had known there was something amiss with that unexpected proposal of marriage when Piet had made it, but she had deliberately blinded herself to the obvious, refused to listen to the voices of doubt in her own head. And he had manipulated her so skilfully, tying her up in bonds of love that she had woven so willingly with her stupid romantic dreams...

It was some moments before she realised that Dirk's embrace had taken on an alarming change. He was no longer comforting her; he was covering her face with heated kisses, murmuring to her in a low, passionate voice, and she could sense a shuddering tension of arousal in him that brought a shocked gasp of protest to her lips as she tore herself out of his arms.

'I'm sorry, I...' What had she done to give him the wrong impression? She should never have let herself be tempted to sob out her troubles on his shoulder like that.

At once his demeanour changed. 'Oh, Miss Heller, forgive me,' he begged, grasping both her hands in

his. 'I permitted myself to get a little carried away.
But please believe me, I would never do anything to
hurt you—I care only for your welfare. If there was
anything I could do... I know this is not the moment
to declare how I feel, but please—if you ever need a
friend, won't you call on me?'

Charlie hesitated, embarrassed at his pathetic plea.
'I... Thank you,' she managed, her throat constricted. 'I'll be all right. It's just...'

'I know. It has been a terrible shock for you. I
would have given anything to have spared you from
such knowledge.'

She shook her head. 'No, I...I prefer to know,'
she said. 'But I would be grateful if you would go
now—I want to be on my own for a little while.'

'Of course.' His eyes were almost misty as they
gazed into hers. 'Please believe that you may always
trust me,' he declared, his voice throbbing with
emotion. 'My heart is forever yours.'

She drew back, her smile a little brittle, and he took
the hint, pausing only to kiss her hands in courtly
gallantry before hurrying over to fetch some file from
Piet's desk, and letting himself out of the apartment.
Charlie heaved a sigh of relief that he was gone,
leaning back against the breakfast bar.

What he had told her was still buzzing in her mind.
All she knew was that somehow she was going to have
to regather the shreds of her dignity and break off
her engagement to Piet. But she wouldn't let him know
that she was leaving because she knew what had been
going on, and was retreating in defeat. She would leave
on her own terms.

* * *

Paris in November had a damp, bedraggled air, far removed from the romance of springtime. Charlie had been here for three months now, living in an artistic little garret in Montmartre. But she hadn't painted a thing. She spent her days walking along the banks of the Seine in the pouring rain, and her evenings waiting on tables in a smoky wine bar near the Opéra.

It had been the easiest thing in the world to engineer a quarrel with Piet. She had gone out, and stayed out very late, until after midnight. And when he had asked, quite reasonably, where she had been she had shrugged, and answered in an offhand manner. He had become annoyed, and she had retaliated with an exaggerated flippancy, until they were shouting at each other, he accusing her of being childish, she declaring that he was boring, that the whole idea of being married was boring. On that intransigent note she had tugged off her ring and tossed it carelessly towards him, and with a great show of packing her bags she had walked out.

Sometimes she would find herself wishing that she had never known the truth, that she had gone ahead and married Piet in blissful romance. Or even that she could have ignored it, and married him anyway. At least then she wouldn't have known this awful dark, gnawing loneliness that seemed to have eaten all the joy and colour out of her life, and left her with only shades of grey.

Struggling wearily up the steep stairs to her little flat one day, the raindrops dripping from the collar of her raincoat and running down her neck, she heard her telephone ringing. But she didn't bother to hurry; it wouldn't be important—she had made no friends in Paris; hardly anyone even knew she was there, except for her father.

But the ringing was persistent, and when at last she picked up the receiver it was a woman's voice she heard. Nothing about the French accent alerted her to what was coming.

'Mademoiselle Heller? I don't know if you will remember me. My name is Janine de Savary. I am a friend of Pieter den Ouden.'

Quite abruptly Charlie's knees had turned to jelly, and she had to sit down on the floor. 'Oh?' was all she could manage, as non-committally as possible.

'Your father gave me your telephone number. I thought you would want to know—Piet has had a heart attack. He is in hospital.'

'*What?*' Her own heart seemed to stop still at the words. 'But what . . . how . . . ?'

'He has been working a great deal too hard.' There was a hint of censure in the voice. 'He always has, of course, but since you left . . . It was against the doctor's orders. He has a hereditary condition, and knows he should avoid too much stress.'

Charlie was shaking, but she was angry that this woman should seem to be blaming her for what had happened. 'So why are you ringing me?' she demanded frostily. 'Why aren't you at his bedside, mopping his brow? You don't expect me to believe he wanted you to ring me?'

'No,' the Frenchwoman conceded patiently. 'He knows nothing of this. I talked it over with his mother, and we agreed that we should at least ask you. Even now he will not agree to slow down—if he continues in this way he is going to kill himself.'

'What makes you think I could persuade him to stop?' Charlie protested, the bitterness welling over. 'You're the one he'd listen to. I'm surprised you're not telling me you've got married to him. What's stopping you? Or aren't you useful enough to the company? Isn't your daddy in the right line of business?'

There was a long pause, and then Janine said, 'I am afraid I do not know what you are talking about. Piet has never asked me to marry him. Once, perhaps, several years ago, I hoped that he might. But if ever we were in love, it has long since subsided into mere friendship—habit, maybe. There is nothing more than that between us now.'

'Oh? I didn't get that impression the first time we met. For a mere friend, you seemed pretty angry at finding me in his apartment.'

'Of course. I was shocked and hurt at what appeared to me a betrayal of the loyalty I would have expected from him. I regret that on that occasion I gave him no opportunity to explain. But later, when I had had some time to reconsider, I realised that I had been a little unfair...'

'So you came back to make it up, behind my back,' Charlie spat nastily. 'Let me give you a little bit of advice, Janine. If you're going to conduct clandestine affairs with married men—or even nearly married men—you really ought to chuck out that perfume of yours. I could smell it all over the apartment when I came in.'

'I did come up to the apartment.' The Frenchwoman's voice was cold and angry too now. 'I had arranged with Piet to collect a number of personal belongings which I had left behind. Lenneke let me in, since Piet was in a meeting.'

'Oh, come on.' Charlie's voice choking. 'Please don't expect me to be so naïve. Dirk van Leiden told me——'

The Frenchwoman snorted. 'That little rat! He has more hands than an octopus, and doesn't know to keep them to himself. Was he trying it on with you too?'

'No, he...he was quite nice...' Suddenly Charlie began to remember again the way she had disliked Dirk so much when she had first met him, the way she had hated the way he used to look at her. But quickly she shook that thought aside—it was irrelevant. 'It was he that opened my eyes to the truth,' she asserted. 'I had been wondering why Piet had suddenly decided he wanted to marry me, out of the blue; but, as Dirk so rightly pointed out, my father was in a position to do the company a great deal of good.'

'If you could believe that of Piet you truly don't deserve him!' came the indignant retort. 'And if you listened to one word Dirk van Leiden ever said then you *are* naïve—more than I ever imagined. He would say anything if he thought it would promote his own interests. No doubt he was hoping that if you split with Piet he could have a chance to take his place.'

'Oh, don't be ridiculous,' Charlie protested scornfully. *'Dirk?'*

'It may seem ridiculous to you, as indeed it does to me,' Janine answered quite reasonably. 'Unfortunately his ego is such that he does not perceive what an ugly little toad he really is. And there are, of course, girls who could overlook every fault for one so wealthy.'

Charlie hesitated, realising the truth of the Frenchwoman's words.

'And as for why Piet wished to marry you,' she went on, 'surely you knew that he was in love with you?'

'No, I didn't know that,' Charlie countered, a note of resentment in her voice. 'He never told me.'

Janine laughed drily. 'That does not surprise me. He is one of those men who find it hard to express their feelings. I expect he would have assumed that it was sufficient that he should ask you to marry him. When you left . . . he would not talk about it, but I know that he was very sad. I and his mother both tried to persuade him not to work so hard, but it seemed that he wanted only to block out everything from his mind. He slept sometimes only a few hours a night, and every waking moment he had to be doing something. I could see weeks ago that he was making himself ill, but he would not listen to any warnings. And now he insists that he will discharge himself from the hospital, against the doctors' advice. Please, Mademoiselle Heller—I know that it is a long way for you to come, and perhaps you are too busy, perhaps there is a new man in your life now. But if once you loved him, please do what you can. Even a telephone call. Persuade him at least to remain until the doctors say he is well enough to leave.'

The tears were coursing freely down Charlie's cheeks. 'Wh . . . which hospital is he in?' she whispered.

'I will give you the location. You have a pen?'

* * *

The clinic was a very exclusive private one; a long, low, modern building, set among shady trees, on the outskirts of Amsterdam. The taxi dropped Charlie outside the wide glass entrance, and she walked inside, her stomach knotted with apprehension.

Pale grey fitted carpets and lots of potted plants gave the reception area a tranquil atmosphere. A girl in a pink uniform looked up as Charlie approached the desk.

'I've come to see Meneer Den Ouden,' she managed a little shakily.

'Ah, yes.' The girl consulted the screen of a computer beside her. 'Are you a relative?'

'I'm ... his fiancée. I've been away— I've only just got back. I came straight from the airport,' she added, feeling a foolish need to explain herself.

The girl smiled. 'Room 210,' she said. 'Take the lift to the second floor, and then turn right through the double doors.'

Charlie nodded and followed the directions given. The clinic seemed almost like an expensive hotel, except for the doctors in their white coats and nurses in smart outfits of grey and pink. The second-floor corridor looked out over a pleasant garden and a quiet lake—a perfect place, if you had to be ill. She counted along the doors until she came to the one marked '210', and then hesitated, unsure.

It had been all very well, talking on the telephone to Janine from Paris; she had allowed herself to be convinced that Piet really *had* loved her. But on the short flight from Le Bourget to Schiphol all the old doubts had begun to return. And besides, after all the terrible things she had said to him when they had quarrelled... But her desperate fear for his health had overruled all her doubts. Her hand was shaking as she tapped on the door.

The brisk voice that called 'Come in' didn't sound sick at all, and the man sitting up in bed, his broad, well-muscled chest bare and bronzed, looked healthy enough to be a total fraud. It was only the hint of shadow beneath those hard grey eyes that betrayed the truth—and the cardiac monitor wired up to his heart.

Clearly a small thing like a heart attack had not been sufficient to stop him working; there was a mobile telephone on the locker beside his bed, and papers all over the bed-cover. She hovered in the doorway, longing to simply run across the room and throw herself into his arms, but the unsmiling look he gave her held her back.

'H...hello,' she managed uncertainly.

'What are you doing here?'

'I... Janine rang and told me you were ill. I just thought I'd...drop by, and see how you were.'

'I am a great deal better than my doctors are prepared to admit. And Janine had no business to ring you.' His voice was brusque to the point of rudeness, but he hadn't actually told her to go away yet. She moved cautiously over to the end of the bed, gripping it tightly with her hands.

'She said you had been working too hard.'

He lifted one straight eyebrow in sardonic query. 'Do you expect that the company will run itself, just because I am stuck in here?'

Charlie sighed with weary frustration; he was just so damned obstinate! 'What if you'd died?' she demanded, the words almost making her wince in pain. 'They'd have had to manage without you then.'

He shrugged her argument aside with cool indifference. 'I have responsibilities. As you made very
clear on the last occasion we spoke, you find such a
notion boring. I'm sorry, but that seems to be an ir-
reconcilable difference between us.'

She shook her head, her emotions spilling over into
tears. 'It wasn't that. You used to say I was being
childish and selfish for wanting you to spend more
time with me, but I was only trying to make you slow
down and relax a bit. I was so afraid for you—afraid
that exactly this would happen. Oh, Piet...' Her voice
broke. 'When Janine rang me I...I just...'

It was no good—she could restrain herself no
longer. In two steps she was round the bed, and as
she crumpled against his chest she felt his arms fold
around her, as warm and strong as ever.

'I didn't mean anything I said that day,' she sobbed
out into the safe hollow of his shoulder. 'You're *not*
boring—you could never be boring. I...I just wanted
to hurt you as much as I possibly could. I thought...I
thought you were still seeing Janine. I'd smelled her
perfume in the flat, and when you said you hadn't
been up there...'

'I hadn't,' he insisted softly.

'I know. She told me what happened—that it was
Lenneke who let her into the apartment. But at the
time I thought...you were lying.'

'Perhaps I should have explained,' he conceded
wryly. 'I simply thought you would not understand.
You were so young, so mercurial... Perhaps I was
wrong—I should have given you more credit. I'm
sorry.'

'It was just that I loved you so much, and I was never quite sure whether you loved me.' Her voice was muffled, and he hugged her tighter.

'But how could you have ever doubted it?' he enquired, genuinely puzzled.

'You never actually told me,' she reminded him wistfully. 'And sometimes I found it hard to understand why you wanted to marry me. I didn't think...I wasn't the sort I imagined you would want to marry—someone a bit more sophisticated, someone who wouldn't embarrass you in front of your friends by acting like a crazy kid.'

He laughed. 'Oh, but what a breath of fresh air you were to my life! I felt as though I was sinking into a premature middle age, and then you came along and turned the whole world every which way.'

She risked a wary peep up at him from beneath her lashes. 'You...you didn't mind?' she asked hopefully.

'It was the best thing that had ever happened to me. But what went wrong then, my little love? Why did you suddenly decide to leave me like that?'

'It was Dirk,' she admitted.

He frowned, puzzled again. 'Dirk van Leiden? But how could he possibly have had anything to do with it?'

She drew a deep breath, aware now that it all sounded rather foolish—as Janine said, she must have been incredibly naïve. 'He said that you wanted to marry me because of my father—because he might be prepared to use his position to help the company if he was your father-in-law. It was the day I left. He had came upstairs to fetch some papers, and ... Piet, don't lose your temper,' she added pleadingly, sitting up and placing a restraining hand against his chest as she felt him tense in anger. 'You shouldn't get excited.'

'Excited?' He seemed ready to throw the sheet aside and leap out of bed. 'I'll kill him! What else did he do?' His eyes were blazing in fury. 'Tell me—did he lay a finger on you?'

'No.' It was best to lie, to try to calm him down. 'Nothing happened, honestly.' She cast an anxious glance at the monitor screen beside the bed, wondering if she should call a nurse—the blips seemed to have accelerated alarmingly.

He laughed wryly and leaned back against the pillow, drawing her into his arms. 'All right, don't worry,' he assured her. 'I don't intend to let that little toad give me a relapse—I will sort him out later.' His voice held a hint of menace that boded ill for the tubby little diamond merchant. He stroked his hand down over her cheek. 'And as for you, you crazy little fool,' he chuckled, 'you held my heart in your hands from the first moment I saw you. I tried very hard to keep it from you, but there was nothing I could do. And look what damage you did when you went away,' he added, smiling as he nodded towards the monitor, now settling to a more regular pattern again. 'You left a great big hole that cannot be mended.'

'I'll mend it,' she promised, gazing up at him as she blinked back the tears. 'All I ever wanted is you. I never wanted to leave you, but I was so unhappy.'

'I'll never make you unhappy again,' he promised softly in return. 'And you are quite right—why should I spend my whole life making money? There must be something more than that. Maybe what I saw in you was the way to help me find it, except that I was so tied up in the habit of working too hard that I could not follow you down those winding flowered paths you wanted to lead me. But I will follow you now,' he added, dropping a light kiss on the tip of her nose. 'From now on I will always have time for you, that I promise—even if it means giving up the company.'

'Giving up the company?' She blinked up at him in surprise.

He nodded, his eyes serious. 'You were right—it has become a monster. And there are things far more valuable to do in life than merely making money. Maria has asked me several times if I would consider becoming the director of her charity, and there are several similar enterprises I would be interested in helping . . .'

'That's beginning to sound like an awful lot of work,' Charlie protested, frowning.

He chuckled. 'Oh, no. You will be my first priority. And our children,' he added, his eyes teasing her.

'Children?' Her own heart skipped. 'Are you sure?'

'Of course.' He smiled wryly. 'You have no need to worry. This stupid condition of mine *is* hereditary, but it is by no means certain that it would be passed on. And, besides, we will bring up our children to value the quality of each day, and never to be so stupid as to make themselves a slave to the clock and the telephone.'

At that moment, as if to challenge him, the mobile telephone beside him buzzed. With a decisive move he reached out and picked it up, and dropped it into the jug of orange juice on the locker. Charlie looked at him in astonishment, and then broke into a gurgle of delighted laughter, wrapping her arms tightly round his neck.

'Oh, I love you,' she cried ecstatically.

'And I love you too.' He drew her up closer on to the bed, and his laughter took on a husky timbre. 'That damned nurse will be round in ten minutes to take my blood-pressure. It doesn't give us much time, but still...' He let his hand slide up beneath the soft lambswool of her sweater, to mould firmly over her small, ripe breast.

'Piet!' she protested, half shocked. 'I really don't think you should——'

He silenced her with a kiss. 'Oh, but I should,' he argued. 'The doctor said I must get regular exercise— and sex is the very best exercise there is. And we really must carry out the doctor's orders—to the letter.'

'But...' Oh, but that kiss was so tempting, and the way he was caressing her breast, with all that magical arousing skill. 'We can't—not here,' she managed breathlessly. 'What if the nurse comes in?'

He laughed, and reluctantly let her go. 'Maybe you are right. I will at once arrange for my discharge.'

'No! Not until the doctor agrees,' she insisted firmly. 'I mean it, Piet. Until the doctor says you're well enough to leave you're staying right here.'

He lifted his eyebrows in teasing amusement. 'Ah. Miss Bossy-Boots, eh? You really think you can last out?'

'Yes.' She wriggled quickly out of his reach before he could catch her and disprove her assertion.

He chuckled. 'Then I shall recover very quickly. It was really not so very serious a heart attack anyway— more of a warning, which I shall now most certainly heed. I want to lead a very long life with you. A hundred years would not be enough for me to finish telling you how much I love you.'

'Mmm.' She allowed him to draw her back into his arms, nestling her head against his strong chest. 'Well, with the wonders of modern medicine, who knows? We may have a hundred years. But even so, you can start telling me right now, if you like. I won't mind the repetition.'

AMSTERDAM—'the Venice of the North'

With its intricate network of canals and bridges, narrow cobbled streets and rows of centuries-old buildings, Amsterdam is considered to be one of the most picturesque and romantic cities of Europe.

Despite its maze of canals, Amsterdam is best depicted as a horseshoe of four main tree-lined canals which are intersected by one main street. The **Singel** (roughly translated as the ring or girdle) is the inner canal and was at one time a fortified boundary protecting the city. The **Herengracht** canal was the most popular canal to live on during the seventeenth century, when rich merchants competed with each other to build the largest and most ornate houses. Decorative gablestones, sculpted on the front, were like 'address plates' telling passersby the owner's name, his occupation and even his town of origin. Although the houses on the **Keizersgracht** are not as spectacular, this canal was named after the great Holy Emperor, Maximilian I, whose lands included the Netherlands. Here, one can see the legendary 'House of the Six Heads'. The heads are said to represent a gang of thieves who broke into the house but were killed by a courageous maid. Smaller houses and warehouses still in use are situated on the **Prinsengracht**—the last main canal.

Moving away from the canal routes, there are famous landmarks that include the city's main square, Dam Square, where the River Amstel was first dammed and thereby giving the city its distinctive name. The royal palace in the square stands out impressively. Originally, it was a town hall, but was then later converted into the royal family's residence. Musical tunes still chime out from the carillon bell tower as they do from the Mint Tower—named so because money was minted there—and the **Westerkerk**, the tallest church tower in the capital, which is distinguished by its large golden orb.

THE ROMANTIC PAST

Legend has it that it was the Balavians who were the first people to settle in the area as they floated down from the Rhine in their log canoes. But it was not until 1275 that the city was officially founded and the citizens were given the right to trade for the first time. Commerce flourished as ships laden with raw goods and spices from the Baltic and the Far East came to the port. Sailors working for the Dutch East Indies companies returned as sea heroes, fascinating their fellow countrymen with tales of their voyages around the world. As diamonds poured into Amsterdam, the country began to prosper. Arts and culture thrived under such a glorious climate, culminating in 'the Golden Age' in the seventeenth century, boasting great artists like Rembrandt,

Vermeer and Frans Hals. Their masterpieces can be seen in the spacious **Rijksmuseum**.

The **Schreierstoren** tower, apart from being a fortification point, has a particularly romantic history. Sailors had to say goodbye to their loved ones, giving this departure point its name—the Weeping Tower or the Tower of Tears. Anne Frank's house is another place of historical interest. It is here that she wrote her famous diary, vividly capturing her thoughts on paper, during the Second World War.

THE ROMANTIC PRESENT—pastimes for lovers...

What better way to see Amsterdam than by canal boat during the day—or even better, why not share a romantic candle-lit dinner on a glass boat at night? Lovers can amble down quaint little streets, lined by traditional Dutch houses and shops. If you look up to their walls, you can see brightly coloured window boxes in the shape of wooden clogs, filled with flowers. From wherever you stand, there is always a flurry of activity in this charming town, from bicycles whizzing past, organ grinders playing pretty tunes, stallholders selling their wares and artists sketching the surrounding scenery.

Visiting a diamond workshop to see how the stones are cut and polished can be an exciting experience.

Perhaps your partner might be tempted to buy one as a token of love?

Bargain-hunting in the city's flea-market is fun—antiques, Delft pottery and pewter all make good souvenirs for the home. Shops, especially in the **Jordaan** area, offer a wide range of presents such as miniature wooden clogs, windmills and dolls in traditional costumes.

The Dutch have a saying—'Here's to good eating in Amsterdam!' Their famous thick pea soup and hash potato dish is mouthwateringly delicious. Most often you will be served cheese such as Edam and Gouda at breakfast and lunch. Desserts are not to be missed—*Flensjes* are thin pancakes with sweet fillings. Or if you prefer something cold and spicy, why not sample *gember met slagroom* which has fresh ginger and cream? Locals enjoy soaking up the relaxed atmosphere in a **brown café**, made out of dark brown wood, where they can enjoy a coffee or an ice-cold beer—perfect after a hard day's work or sightseeing!

Festivals and parades throughout the year make Amsterdam a lively and colourful town. At the beginning of September, a large floral parade comes from the flower town, Aalsmeer, to the capital with a burst of music and people. By mid-November, the Dutch Father Christmas, St Nicolaas, arrives by boat from Spain and rides a white horse around town. Parcels Night, a family festival, is celebrated the day before St Nicolaas's return to Spain.

DID YOU KNOW THAT...?

* the Dutch currency is called the **gulden** or the **guilder**.

* Amsterdam does not have a government—it is in the Hague.

* there are more canals in Amsterdam than in Venice.

* Amsterdam is the largest industrial city in Holland and one of the main financial centres of the world.

* the most popular form of transport is by bicycle rather than car.

* Dutch people are excellent at languages: English, French and German are just a few of the languages they speak.

* the way to say 'I love you' in Dutch is: *'Ik hou van jou'*.

LOOK OUT FOR ONE TITLE EVERY MONTH IN OUR SERIES OF EUROPEAN ROMANCES:

MASK OF DECEPTION: Sara Wood (Italy)
Why was Lucenzo Salviati so determined that Meredith leave Venice? Was it because of her family's secrets—or the intense attraction between them?

VIKING MAGIC: Angela Wells (Denmark)
Gina was in Copenhagen to rescue her wayward sister, but she landed in the arms of Rune Christensen instead—who aroused feelings she'd *never* felt before!

LOVE OF MY HEART: Emma Richmond (Eire)
Ellie wanted to settle an old family score, and Feargal agreed that she should—though Ellie hadn't bargained on paying *him*, or with her heart!

DARK SUNLIGHT: Patricia Wilson (Spain)
Felipe de Santis was used to giving orders—and Maggie to doing things her way. There was a battle of wills in store...would Felipe stop at nothing to get what he wanted?

DESIGNED TO ANNOY: Elizabeth Oldfield (Germany)
Sophie was left holding someone else's baby—but she was determined to track down Dieter von Lossigen, and have him shoulder his fatherly responsibilities!

Next Month's Romances

Each month you can choose from a wide variety of romance with Mills & Boon. Below are the new titles to look out for next month, why not ask either Mills & Boon Reader Service or your Newsagent to reserve you a copy of the titles you want to buy — just tick the titles you would like and either post to Reader Service or take it to any Newsagent and ask them to order your books.

Please save me the following titles:	Please tick	✓
BREAKING POINT	Emma Darcy	
SUCH DARK MAGIC	Robyn Donald	
AFTER THE BALL	Catherine George	
TWO-TIMING MAN	Roberta Leigh	
HOST OF RICHES	Elizabeth Power	
MASK OF DECEPTION	Sara Wood	
A SOLITARY HEART	Amanda Carpenter	
AFTER THE FIRE	Kay Gregory	
BITTERSWEET YESTERDAYS	Kate Proctor	
YESTERDAY'S PASSION	Catherine O'Connor	
NIGHT OF THE SCORPION	Rosemary Carter	
NO ESCAPING LOVE	Sharon Kendrick	
OUTBACK LEGACY	Elizabeth Duke	
RANSACKED HEART	Jayne Bauling	
STORMY REUNION	Sandra K. Rhoades	
A POINT OF PRIDE	Liz Fielding	

If you would like to order these books in addition to your regular subscription from Mills & Boon Reader Service please send £1.70 per title to: Mills & Boon Reader Service, P.O. Box 236, Croydon, Surrey, CR9 3RU, quote your Subscriber No:....................................... (If applicable) and complete the name and address details below. Alternatively, these books are available from many local Newsagents including W.H.Smith, J.Menzies, Martins and other paperback stockists from 12th March 1993.

Name:..

Address:..

....Post Code:...........................

To Retailer: If you would like to stock M&B books please contact your regular book/magazine wholesaler for details.

You may be mailed with offers from other reputable companies as a result of this application. If you would rather not take advantage of these opportunities please tick box ☐

4 FREE

Romances
and 2 FREE gifts
just for you!

*You can enjoy all the
heartwarming emotion of true love for FREE!
Discover the heartbreak and the happiness, the emotion and
the tenderness of the modern relationships in
Mills & Boon Romances.*

*We'll send you 4 captivating Romances as a special offer from
Mills & Boon Reader Service, along with the chance to have
6 Romances delivered to your door each month.*

Claim your FREE books and gifts overleaf...

An irresistible offer from Mills & Boon

Here's a personal invitation from Mills & Boon Reader Service, to become a regular reader of Romances. To welcome you, we'd like you to have 4 books, a CUDDLY TEDDY and a special MYSTERY GIFT absolutely FREE.

Then you could look forward each month to receiving 6 brand new Romances, delivered to your door, postage and packing free! Plus our free Newsletter featuring author news, competitions, special offers and much more.

This invitation comes with no strings attached. You may cancel or suspend your subscription at any time, and still keep your free books and gifts.

It's so easy. Send no money now. Simply fill in the coupon below and post it to -
Reader Service, FREEPOST, PO Box 236, Croydon, Surrey CR9 9EL.

-------------------------------- **NO STAMP REQUIRED** --------------------------------

Free Books Coupon

Yes! Please rush me 4 free Romances and 2 free gifts! Please also reserve me a Reader Service subscription. If I decide to subscribe I can look forward to receiving 6 brand new Romances each month for just £10.20, postage and packing free. If I choose not to subscribe I shall write to you within 10 days - I can keep the books and gifts whatever I decide. I may cancel or suspend my subscription at any time. I am over 18 years of age.

Ms/Mrs/Miss/Mr_____ EP31R

Address _____

_____

Postcode_____Signature _____